TEST YOUR PLAY AS DECLARER

Any reader who studies this book carefully will certainly become much more adept at playing out a hand.

There are 89 hands here. Each emphasizes a particular point in declarer play. The solution to each problem explains how and why a declarer should handle his cards in a certain way. The authors' comments are quite enlightening, and they lead the reader into new dimensions.

Most of the hands are taken from actual tournaments.

TEST YOUR PLAY
as
DECLARER

♠ ♡ ♣ ◇

Paul Lukacs and Jeff Rubens

HART PUBLISHING COMPANY, INC.
NEW YORK CITY

INTRODUCTION

This book is a collection of problems in declarer play. These are *not* double-dummy problems. The solution in each case requires logical thought and the correct application of a sound principle of card play.

The reader can improve his techniques in declarer play by examining each situation carefully. After the reader has made his decision, the solution will tell him whether or not he arrived at the correct method of play. The solution will also explain the basic principle involved.

The bidding is significant only in those situations in which the East-West bidding—or the lack of it—must be considered.

The only conventions used are (1) Stayman and (2) an artificial two-club opening which shows a strong hand, not necessarily in clubs. Here, a negative two-diamond response will indicate a very weak hand, not necessarily relating to diamonds.

Although the reader may want to review the North-South bidding, it is not necessary to thoroughly understand the bidding in order to attack the playing problem. And it is certainly unnecessary to approve the bidding, since some of the bidding is poor.

We all get to inferior contracts now and then, and any practical manual of play must include poor contracts as well as good ones.

The solution to each problem is found directly on the page after the presentation.

These are not easy problems; quite the contrary, some of them are admittedly difficult.

PAUL LUKACS
JEFF RUBENS

New York, 1976

PROBLEM 1

Rubber bridge
East-West vulnerable

NORTH
♠ A 8 6
♡ 6 2
◇ 10 4
♣ A 7 6 4 3 2

SOUTH
♠ 9 5
♡ A Q 5 4
◇ A J 3
♣ K Q 9 8

SOUTH	WEST	NORTH	EAST
1 NT	Pass	3 NT	Pass
Pass	Pass		

West leads the spade king.

Plan the play.

SOLUTION 1

```
          ♠ A 8 6
          ♡ 6 2
          ◇ 10 4
          ♣ A 7 6 4 3 2
♠ K Q J 10 3              ♠ 7 4 2
♡ K 10 8                  ♡ J 9 7 3
◇ Q 5                     ◇ K 9 8 7 6 2
♣ J 10 5                  ♣ —
          ♠ 9 5
          ♡ A Q 5 4
          ◇ A J 3
          ♣ K Q 9 8
```

South seems to have nine easy tricks, but there is a fly in the ointment: the club suit is blocked. The block will not prevent running the suit if the opponents' clubs are split 2-1. In that case, declarer can win the first two club tricks with the king and queen, exhausting the East-West clubs, then win the third trick in clubs with the nine, and finally overtake the eight with the ace.

However, a 3-0 club split will doom this plan, and declarer should take measures to guard against this possibility. The simplest way to overcome the problem is to discard one of South's clubs. This can be accomplished only through one suit, spades, so South should duck the opening lead.

If West leads another spade, declarer ducks again and can now take nine tricks by playing king-queen-ace of clubs and throwing his last club on the spade ace.

If West shifts, declarer wins and ducks another spade himself, achieving the same position.

PROBLEM 2

Rubber bridge
East-West vulnerable

NORTH
♠ 8 4 3
♡ —
♢ 8 6 4 2
♣ K Q J 10 8 4

SOUTH
♠ A K Q 5 2
♡ J 9 6 4
♢ A K
♣ A 3

SOUTH	WEST	NORTH	EAST
2 ♠	Pass	3 ♣	Pass
3 ♡	Pass	3 ♠	Pass
4 ♢	Pass	4 ♠	Pass
6 ♠	Pass	Pass	Pass

West leads the heart three.

Plan the play.

SOLUTION 2

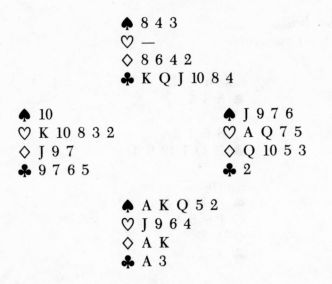

♠ 8 4 3
♡ —
◇ 8 6 4 2
♣ K Q J 10 8 4

♠ 10
♡ K 10 8 3 2
◇ J 9 7
♣ 9 7 6 5

♠ J 9 7 6
♡ A Q 7 5
◇ Q 10 5 3
♣ 2

♠ A K Q 5 2
♡ J 9 6 4
◇ A K
♣ A 3

After ruffing the opening lead in dummy, declarer should lead a trump from dummy and play low from his own hand. The defenders can win this trick, but declarer will take the rest (barring a 5-0 break in a black suit). A further heart lead can be ruffed in dummy.

This play gives up an overtrick when trumps break 3-2, but preserves the contract when trumps break 4-1. If declarer tries to draw trumps by leading high ones, a 4-1 trump break defeats him.

If South tries to ruff two hearts and throw another on a club, he may be frustrated by a 4-1 club break. The immediate duck in spades avoids all these dangers.

PROBLEM 3

Rubber bridge
East-West vulnerable

NORTH
♠ A Q
♡ A J
♢ K Q 8 4 3
♣ K Q 10 3

SOUTH
♠ K J
♡ K Q
♢ A 10 5 2
♣ A 9 5 4 2

SOUTH	WEST	NORTH	EAST
1 NT	Pass	7 NT	Pass
Pass	Pass		

West leads the spade ten.

Plan the play.

♠

SOLUTION 3

```
                    ♠ A Q
                    ♡ A J
                    ◊ K Q 8 4 3
                    ♣ K Q 10 3
♠ 10 9 8 7                            ♠ 6 5 4 3 2
♡ 10                                 ♡ 9 8 7 6 5 4 3 2
◊ J 9 7 6                            ◊ —
♣ J 8 7 6                            ♣ —
                    ♠ K J
                    ♡ K Q
                    ◊ A 10 5 2
                    ♣ A 9 5 4 2
```

This contract looks easy, but is actually tricky. The critical fact is that the club and diamond suits have different properties. Declarer is sure to pick up the club suit even if one opponent has all four missing clubs—if he leads the king or queen first. But in diamonds, if the suit is 4-0 declarer must guess how to play the suit—king or queen first if he judges East may have all four; ace first, if he judges West may hold all four.

Declarer should reserve his decision in diamonds as long as possible to get information to help him resolve this guess. After playing clubs and discovering West has all four, it cannot hurt him to play off his major-suit winners. In the course of doing this, he discovers, with the cards as in the diagram, that East started with eight hearts and at least two spades, so it is impossible for him to have started with four diamonds. So, declarer should cash the diamond ace first.

An optimal play sequence would be: spade ace, club king, heart king, club finesse, heart ace, spade king, diamond ace, diamond finesse, club queen, clubs in the South hand, diamond.

PROBLEM 4

Rubber bridge
Both sides vulnerable

NORTH
♠ 10 3 2
♡ 10 4
♢ K 4
♣ 10 8 6 5 4 2

SOUTH
♠ A K Q 6 5 4
♡ A K 8 7
♢ A 5
♣ A

SOUTH	WEST	NORTH	EAST
2 ♠	Pass	2 NT	Pass
3 ♡	Pass	3 ♠	Pass
4 ♢	Pass	4 ♠	Pass
5 ♣	Pass	5 ♢	Pass
6 ♠	Pass	Pass	Pass

West leads the spade jack.

Plan the play.

SOLUTION 4

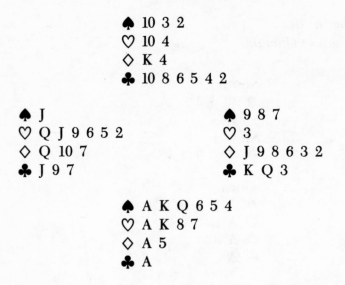

```
                ♠ 10 3 2
                ♡ 10 4
                ◇ K 4
                ♣ 10 8 6 5 4 2

♠ J                             ♠ 9 8 7
♡ Q J 9 6 5 2                   ♡ 3
◇ Q 10 7                        ◇ J 9 8 6 3 2
♣ J 9 7                         ♣ K Q 3

                ♠ A K Q 6 5 4
                ♡ A K 8 7
                ◇ A 5
                ♣ A
```

When a contract seems secure, declarer should think what might possibly go wrong. Even though trumps are 3-1, there will be no problem if a high heart is not ruffed, since dummy's ruffing trump is a high one.

When declarer draws a second round of trumps and discovers that East holds the missing trump, he should play to neutralize the effect of the ruff of a high heart. The correct play is to draw two trumps, then cash one high heart, then lead a diamond to dummy in order to lead a heart through East. If East ruffs, declarer follows low, and later ruffs his remaining low heart in dummy. If East discards, declarer safely wins his second high heart and ruffs a heart loser in dummy.

Not taking a second round of trumps would be the best play for seven, not six.

PROBLEM 5

Rubber bridge
East-West vulnerable

NORTH
♠ A 10 8
♡ Q 7 6 2
◇ K 5 4
♣ J 9 3

SOUTH
♠ K Q J
♡ J 9 4
◇ 9 6 3
♣ A Q 10 5

SOUTH	WEST	NORTH	EAST
1 ♣	Pass	1 ♡	Pass
1 NT	Pass	Pass	Pass

West leads the queen, jack, and deuce of diamonds. East wins the third diamond with the ace, and shifts to a spade.

Plan the play.

SOLUTION 5

♠ A 10 8
♡ Q 7 6 2
◇ K 5 4
♣ J 9 3

♠ 6 5 4 3 2   ♠ 9 7
♡ A 10 5   ♡ K 8 3
◇ Q J 10 2   ◇ A 8 7
♣ 2   ♣ K 8 7 6 4

♠ K Q J
♡ J 9 4
◇ 9 6 3
♣ A Q 10 5

It would be poor strategy for declarer to try for hearts, because even if he could set up two heart tricks he would still need the club finesse to make his contract.

Instead, declarer should depend on the club finesse. But he must be careful. To lead the three would make it impossible to repeat the finesse. To lead the jack would squeeze the South hand in clubs if East, properly, ducked. If South plays the five, he must win the next club in his hand; if South plays the ten, East has a fourth-round stopper.

The correct play is to lead the nine from dummy, underplaying with the five if East ducks. Then lead the jack from dummy, underplaying with the ten. However East defends, declarer makes four club tricks and his contract.

My Bucket List

PROBLEM 6

Rubber bridge
Neither side vulnerable

NORTH
♠ 5 4 3
♡ A 6
♢ A J 9 8
♣ A 7 6 4

SOUTH
♠ A Q 2
♡ 3
♢ K Q 10 6 3 2
♣ K Q 5

SOUTH	WEST	NORTH	EAST
1 ♢	Pass	3 ♢	Pass
3 ♠	Pass	4 ♣	Pass
4 NT	Pass	5 ♠	Pass
5 NT	Pass	6 ♣	Pass
6 ♢	Pass	Pass	Pass

West leads the heart jack.

Plan the play.

SOLUTION 6

♠ 5 4 3
♡ A 6
◇ A J 9 8
♣ A 7 6 4

♠ K 7 6
♡ J 10 8 7 2
◇ 5
♣ J 9 8 2

♠ J 10 9 8
♡ K Q 9 5 4
◇ 7 4
♣ 10 3

♠ A Q 2
♡ 3
◇ K Q 10 6 3 2
♣ K Q 5

There are two main chances for the contract: a 3-3 club split, and a spade finesse.

If the spades are tried first, the only extra chance would be an unlikely black-suit squeeze. But if the clubs are tried first, declarer has an extra chance.

He should draw trumps while ruffing dummy's low heart. Then as South tries to run clubs and West shows up with four clubs, South can lead a fourth round from dummy, discarding a losing spade. If West wins this trick, he is endplayed: he must lead into the spade A-Q, or concede a ruff-and-sluff.

PROBLEM 7

Rubber bridge
Both sides vulnerable

NORTH
♠ J 4 3 2
♡ 8 6 4
◇ J 9 3
♣ A J 6

SOUTH
♠ K Q 10 9 7
♡ A 5 2
◇ 10 8 6
♣ K 10

SOUTH	WEST	NORTH	EAST
1 ♠	Pass	2 ♠	Pass
Pass	Pass	Pass	

West leads the heart king.

Plan the play.

SOLUTION 7

♠ J 4 3 2
♥ 8 6 4
♦ J 9 3
♣ A J 6

♠ A 5   ♠ 8 6
♥ K Q 9   ♥ J 10 7 3
♦ 7 5 4 2   ♦ A K Q
♣ Q 8 7 3   ♣ 9 5 4 2

♠ K Q 10 9 7
♥ A 5 2
♦ 10 8 6
♣ K 10

It is worth the risk of an extra 100 points (down two instead of down one) to try to make the contract. The value of making two spades is not merely the 60 points that appear below the line but also the avoidance of paying a penalty of 100, and the increased chance to win the rubber bonus of 500.

After winning the heart ace—there is no point to a hold-up—declarer should realize that the defense can take six tricks if they are allowed in at once with the ace of trumps. Before touching trumps, declarer must, therefore, take the club finesse to develop a discard for a red-suit loser, even though such play risks a two-trick set.

It is worth the risk of an extra 100 points (down two instead of down one) to try to make the contract. The value of making two spades is not merely the 60 points that appear below the line but also the avoidance of paying a penalty of 100, and the increased chance to win the rubber bonus of 500.

PROBLEM 8

Rubber bridge
East-West vulnerable

NORTH
♠ J 6 5
♡ K J 9
♢ A Q 9 6 4
♣ K J

SOUTH
♠ K Q 9
♡ A 10 8 6
♢ K 8 7 5
♣ A Q

SOUTH	WEST	NORTH	EAST
1 NT	Pass	4 NT	Pass
6 NT	Pass	Pass	Pass

West leads the club ten.

Plan the play.

SOLUTION 8

♠ J 6 5
♥ K J 9
♦ A Q 9 6 4
♣ K J

♠ 10 8 7 3 2
♥ 7 5
♦ J 10 3 2
♣ 10 9

♠ A 4
♥ Q 4 3 2
♦ —
♣ 8 7 6 5 4 3 2

♠ K Q 9
♥ A 10 8 6
♦ K 8 7 5
♣ A Q

Whenever he chooses to play diamonds (either at trick two or after knocking out the ace of spades), declarer should lead the king first. He cannot pick up the suit if East has all four diamonds, but playing the king (as opposed to the ace or queen) caters to West holding all four.

After the diamonds are taken care of and the spade ace is dislodged, declarer must guess the queen of hearts. He should postpone this play as long as possible, playing the other suits to get a count of the East-West hands.

With the cards as they are in the diagram, East shows up with two cards in spades and diamonds compared with West's nine cards in spades and diamonds. Thus, the odds greatly favor East holding the heart queen.

PROBLEM 9

Rubber bridge
Neither side vulnerable

NORTH
♠ 5 4
♡ K 10 6 3
◇ K 8 3
♣ A K J 10

SOUTH
♠ Q J 10 9 7 2
♡ 2
◇ A Q 4
♣ Q 8 5

SOUTH	WEST	NORTH	EAST
—	—	1 ♣	Pass
1 ♠	Pass	1 NT	Pass
3 ♠	Pass	4 ♠	Pass
Pass	Pass		

West leads the heart queen.

Plan the play.

♠ 5 4
♡ K 10 6 3
◇ K 8 3
♣ A K J 10

♠ A 8 6 3   ♠ K
♡ Q J 9 7   ♡ A 8 5 4
◇ 9 5   ◇ J 10 7 6 2
♣ 4 3 2   ♣ 9 7 6

♠ Q J 10 9 7 2
♡ 2
◇ A Q 4
♣ Q 8 5

Declarer needs no heart trick for his contract, but he needs a heart stopper to prevent the defense from forcing the strong trumps out of the closed hand. If declarer ducks the first trick, the defense is helpless.

If West leads another heart—which is as good a play as any—that lead establishes a heart trick in dummy. The South hand can be forced only twice. The contract is secure, even against a 4-1 trump break.

If declarer covers with the king of hearts at trick one, he seals his own doom. East wins and returns a heart, which South must ruff. East wins the first spade with the king, and returns another heart, which South must ruff again. Now, when West gets in with the ace of spades, West can lead yet another heart, establishing his spade eight as the setting trick.

PROBLEM 10

Rubber bridge
Both sides vulnerable

NORTH
♠ A K 4 3
♡ 2
♢ A K 4 2
♣ K Q J 10

SOUTH
♠ 7
♡ A 10 8 6
♢ 6 5 3
♣ A 9 8 7 5

SOUTH	WEST	NORTH	EAST
Pass	Pass	1 ♢	Pass
1 ♡	Pass	2 ♠	Pass
3 ♣	Pass	4 ♣	Pass
4 ♡	Pass	4 NT	Pass
5 ♡	Pass	7 ♣	Pass
Pass	Pass		

West leads the club six.

Plan the play.

SOLUTION 10

♠ A K 4 3
♥ 2
♦ A K 4 2
♣ K Q J 10

♠ J 9 5   ♠ Q 10 8 6 2
♥ K J 9 5 4   ♥ Q 7 3
♦ Q J 10 9   ♦ 8 7
♣ 6   ♣ 4 3 2

♠ 7
♥ A 10 8 6
♦ 6 5 3
♣ A 9 8 7 5

With five top tricks in the side suits, declarer needs
eight trump tricks. The simplest plan is to ruff three hearts
in dummy, returning to the closed hand with spade ruffs.
In order to avoid having his diamond winners ruffed,
declarer should take them at once—it will be riskier to try
to take them later because the defense may have a chance
to discard while declarer is ruffing back and forth. So
South should win the opening lead, cash his high diamonds, and crossruff the balance with high trumps.

Note how the play would go in the absence of taking
the high diamonds early: club ten, heart ace, heart ruff,
spade ace-king throwing a diamond, spade ruff, heart
ruff, spade ruff, heart ruff *on which East throws a dia-*
mond. Now dummy is stuck with all diamonds and East
ruffs the second high diamond to defeat the contract.

PROBLEM 11

Matchpoints
East-West vulnerable

> NORTH
> ♠ 9 8 2
> ♡ —
> ◇ A K J 10 6 3
> ♣ K Q J 10
>
> SOUTH
> ♠ A 5 4
> ♡ K J 4 2
> ◇ 9 8 2
> ♣ A 6 4

SOUTH	WEST	NORTH	EAST
1 ◇	1 ♡	6 ◇	(All Pass)

You don't like the bidding? Neither do we. West leads the queen of spades, East playing the ten.

Plan the play.

SOLUTION 11

♠ 9 8 2
♡ —
♢ A K J 10 6 3
♣ K Q J 10

♠ Q J 6 3   ♠ K 10 7
♡ A Q 10 7 5 3   ♡ 9 8 6
♢ Q   ♢ 7 5 4
♣ 8 5   ♣ 9 7 3 2

♠ A 5 4
♡ K J 4 2
♢ 9 8 2
♣ A 6 4

Even if the diamond suit can be brought in, South is in danger of losing two spade tricks. If trumps are 2-2, all is well. But if trumps are 3-1, he must ruff a spade in the closed hand after taking a discard in clubs. This play will succeed if one defender (almost certainly East) holds three diamonds and four clubs.

To give himself the best opportunity to overcome a 3-1 trump split, South should *duck the first spade.* Upon winning the spade return he can take two rounds of trumps, then play on clubs (discarding a spade), ruff a spade, and finally return to dummy to draw the remaining trump.

If South wins the first spade, he must give up a spade trick before ruffing a spade. If he has drawn two rounds of trumps, East will win the spade and lead a third round, killing the ruff. Attempting to circumvent this by drawing only one trump will lose the contract if West, with queen doubleton of diamonds and two clubs, has the acumen to put up the queen of diamonds on the first trump lead—not a difficult play.

PROBLEM 12

IMP Scoring
East-West vulnerable

NORTH
♠ A 3
♡ 5 4 3 2
◇ A 5 4
♣ A K 10 9

SOUTH
♠ K Q 10 6 5 4
♡ A 7
◇ 8 2
♣ J 3 2

SOUTH	WEST	NORTH	EAST
—	—	1 ♣	Pass
1 ♠	Pass	1 NT	Pass
3 ♠	Pass	4 ♠	(All Pass)

West leads the queen of hearts, East playing the eight.

Plan the play.

SOLUTION 12

- ♠ A 3
- ♡ 5 4 3 2
- ◇ A 5 4
- ♣ A K 10 9

♠ J 9 7 2	♠ 8
♡ Q J 10 9	♡ K 8 6
◇ K 9 7 6	◇ Q J 10 3
♣ 4	♣ Q 8 7 6 5

- ♠ K Q 10 6 5 4
- ♡ A 7
- ◇ 8 2
- ♣ J 3 2

If the spades come in, there is no problem. If not, declarer must plan to discard his losing diamond on the fourth round of clubs. But the defenders may get to their diamond trick first.

To minimize this danger, declarer should plan to refuse the club finesse. Taking the club finesse will lose the contract if East holds the queen of clubs and the defender with the long trump holds fewer than three clubs. If, however, declarer plays ace, king, and another club (before the ace of diamonds is removed) he is assured a chance to discard on the fourth club.

This line of play will insure the contract if clubs are four-two or better, or the club queen is singleton (unless West holds all five trumps). But it can be improved still further. Declarer should take the ace of hearts and lead a club to the ace at once. Then he draws three rounds of trumps and leads a second club. If West started with four trumps and a singleton club he cannot profitably ruff, and declarer still gets a chance to discard on the fourth club. Leading a club to the ace at the second trick has nothing to lose, for the contract is safe if either opponent ruffs.

PROBLEM 13

Rubber bridge
Neither side vulnerable

NORTH
♠ Q 8 2
♡ J 9 7 5
◇ A 2
♣ Q 6 4 2

SOUTH
♠ K 6 4
♡ A Q 10 6
◇ 6 3
♣ A K 10 8

SOUTH	WEST	NORTH	EAST
1 ♡	1 ♠	2 ♡	Pass
2 NT	Pass	4 ♡	(All Pass)

The first four tricks are:
   Diamond king, deuce, four, three.
   Diamond queen, *ace,* five, six.
   Heart nine, king, *ace,* deuce.
   Heart queen, three, five, diamond seven.

Plan the play.

SOLUTION 13

♠ Q 8 2
♡ J 9 7 5
◇ A 2
♣ Q 6 4 2

♠ J 10 9 5 3   ♠ A 7
♡ 8 4 3 2   ♡ K
◇ K Q J 8   ◇ 10 9 7 5 4
♣ —   ♣ J 9 7 5 3

♠ K 6 4
♡ A Q 10 6
◇ 6 3
♣ A K 10 8

Even though South is certain to pick up the club suit (West can hardly have four clubs), he needs a spade trick to score game. Thus, the spade ace must be dislodged before trumps are drawn.

If declarer knocks out the ace of spades before drawing trumps, the only danger to the contract is a club ruff. If either opponent is void of clubs it is surely West (who has four hearts, presumably four or more spades, and at least two diamonds). Therefore South should play the six of hearts, win as cheaply as possible in dummy, and lead spades through East. If East takes the ace of spades and gives West a club ruff, the contract is still safe because declarer now has two spade tricks. If South is allowed to win the king of spades he can draw the last trump and proceed to tackle clubs. And if *West* holds the ace of spades, there is no danger to the contract in any event.

PROBLEM 14

Matchpoints.
Neither side vulnerable

NORTH
♠ 5 2
♡ A 5 3
◇ K 8 5 3 2
♣ A 5 3

SOUTH
♠ A K 6
♡ K Q 7 4 2
◇ A 9
♣ K 7 6

SOUTH	WEST	NORTH	EAST
—	—	1 ◇	Pass
2 ♡	Pass	3 ♡	Pass
4 NT	Pass	5 ♡	Pass
5 NT	Pass	6 ◇	Pass
7 ♡	Pass	Pass	Pass

West leads the club ten.

Plan the play.

SOLUTION 14

```
                    ♠ 5 2
                    ♡ A 5 3
                    ◇ K 8 5 3 2
                    ♣ A 5 3
♠ J 9 7                             ♠ Q 10 8 4 3
♡ J 9 8                             ♡ 10 6
◇ Q J 7 6                           ◇ 10 4
♣ 10 9 8                            ♣ Q J 4 2
                    ♠ A K 6
                    ♡ K Q 7 4 2
                    ◇ A 9
                    ♣ K 7 6
```

Declarer must assume trumps are 3-2. If diamonds are 3-3, there is no problem. There is also no problem (and no contract) if diamonds are 5-1 or 6-0.

Therefore, declarer should plan to succeed whenever possible if diamonds break 4-2. In this event two ruffs will be required to establish a long diamond in dummy and a spade ruff is also necessary (for the thirteenth trick). So the basic plan must be: win the club king (retaining the club ace as a late entry to cash the long diamond), take the ace-king of diamonds, ruff a diamond, ruff a spade, ruff a diamond, draw trumps, lead a club to the ace, and cash the good diamond in dummy.

As a safety play, declarer should cash the king and ace of hearts before attacking diamonds. This will avoid an overruff if West holds doubletons in both red suits, and an uppercut if (as in the diagram) East holds two doubletons. This line also succeeds if East has three hearts and two diamonds.

PROBLEM 15

Rubber bridge
East-West vulnerable

> NORTH
> ♠ A 6
> ♡ 10 2
> ◇ K 7 6 5 4
> ♣ A K 6 2
>
> SOUTH
> ♠ K J 9
> ♡ K 9 4 3
> ◇ A Q 2
> ♣ 7 5 3

SOUTH	WEST	NORTH	EAST
—	—	1 ◇	Pass
2 NT	Pass	3 ♣	Pass
3 NT	(All Pass)		

West leads the spade three.

Plan the play.

```
                    ♠ A 6
                    ♡ 10 2
                    ◇ K 7 6 5 4
                    ♣ A K 6 2

♠ Q 10 4 3 2                        ♠ 8 7 5
♡ A Q 6                             ♡ J 8 7 5
◇ 8                                 ◇ J 10 9 3
♣ Q 10 8 4                          ♣ J 9

                    ♠ K J 9
                    ♡ K 9 4 3
                    ◇ A Q 2
                    ♣ 7 5 3
```

South may need three spade tricks for his contract so he
should win the first trick in his own hand. With the spade
winners blocked, there is now the danger of being blocked out of the South hand if diamonds split badly. If, for
example, the cards are distributed as shown in the diagram, South will be badly placed if he cashes the ace and
queen of diamonds immediately.

Instead, South should play just one high diamond from
his hand. (If diamonds break five-zero South has time to
change his plan of attack.) He should then play a spade to
the ace and duck a diamond. Now he can use the remaining high diamond in the closed hand as an entry to cash
the high spade, and use the high clubs in dummy to
provide access to the rest of the diamond suite.

PROBLEM 16

Matchpoints
North-South vulnerable

NORTH
♠ A 10 4
♡ A 3 2
♢ A 6 3
♣ 9 8 6 5

SOUTH
♠ 7 6 5 2
♡ K Q J 10 9
♢ K 10
♣ A 2

SOUTH	WEST	NORTH	EAST
—	—	1 ♣	Pass
1 ♡	Pass	1 NT	Pass
4 ♡	(All Pass)		

Heart four, deuce, seven,?

Plan the play.

SOLUTION 16

♠ A 10 4
♡ A 3 2
◇ A 6 3
♣ 9 8 6 5

♠ K Q 9 8　　　　　　　♠ J 3
♡ 8 6 5 4　　　　　　　♡ 7
◇ Q 9 2　　　　　　　　◇ J 8 7 5 4
♣ Q 7　　　　　　　　　♣ K J 10 4 3

♠ 7 6 5 2
♡ K Q J 10 9
◇ K 10
♣ A 2

If spades do not split 3-3, declarer will require a spade ruff in dummy for his tenth trick. Although the unfavorable trump lead puts the defense one step ahead in the race, declarer should play spades at once in the hope the defender with four spades has only two trumps (and thus cannot play a third round of trumps when he wins the third round of spades).

There is the additional possibility that hearts are 4-1 and the defender with the singleton heart can be forced to win one of the defensive spade tricks. Accordingly, declarer should win the first trick in the closed hand and finesse the spade ten. With cards as shown, West cannot win both spade tricks—but he can if declarer plays ace and another space.

The only danger in this line is that spades break 5-1. This is highly unlikely in view of the absence of a spade overcall.

PROBLEM 17

Rubber bridge
North-South vulnerable

> **NORTH**
> ♠ 5 3
> ♡ 6 5
> ◇ A J 10 9 5 4 2
> ♣ 10 9
>
> **SOUTH**
> ♠ A Q 7
> ♡ A Q 2
> ◇ K 3
> ♣ A K Q 6 5

SOUTH	WEST	NORTH	EAST
—	—	3 ◇	Pass
6 NT	(All pass)		

West leads the spade jack, East playing the six.

Plan the play.

SOLUTION 17

♠ 5 3
♡ 6 5
♢ A J 10 9 5 4 2
♣ 10 9

♠ J 10 9   ♠ K 8 6 4 2
♡ K 10 9 7   ♡ J 8 4 3
♢ 6   ♢ Q 8 7
♣ J 8 7 4 2   ♣ 3

♠ A Q 7
♡ A Q 2
♢ K 3
♣ A K Q 6 5

Assuming diamonds are not divided 4-0, South can make certain of his contract by leading a diamond to the jack. If *either* opponent wins the queen, declarer takes the rest easily. If the jack of diamonds holds, declarer returns to his king of diamonds and leads a low club, forcing entry to dummy in clubs. In any event, declarer will take 12 tricks.

Leading the king of diamonds first is likely to prove superior only if West holds all four missing diamonds. However, the chances of making the contract in that situation are not bright, even if South starts with the king of diamonds. Playing to the jack of diamonds guards against the much more likely possibility that an opponent holds three diamonds to the queen.

PROBLEM 18

Rubber bridge
North-South vulnerable

NORTH
- ♠ A Q J 10 9
- ♡ 10 8
- ◇ A 10 9 4
- ♣ K Q

SOUTH
- ♠ K 8
- ♡ A Q 9 7
- ◇ Q 8 7
- ♣ A J 10 9

SOUTH	WEST	NORTH	EAST
1 NT	Pass	3 ♠	Pass
3 NT	Pass	6 NT	(All pass)

West leads the club eight.

Plan the play.

SOLUTION 18

♠ A Q J 10 9
♡ 10 8
♢ A 10 9 4
♣ K Q

♠ 4 3   ♠ 7 6 5 2
♡ K J 3   ♡ 6 5 4 2
♢ J 6 3 2   ♢ K 5
♣ 8 7 6 5   ♣ 4 3 2

♠ K 8
♡ A Q 9 7
♢ Q 8 7
♣ A J 10 9

South must decide whether to begin his red suits with diamonds or hearts. By starting hearts, South wins if one of two finesses in hearts succeeds or if either opponent holds the singleton king of diamonds.

Starting diamonds also gives declarer the chance to win one of two finesses, but with an important difference. If the first diamond play is from dummy, South can finesse against either the king or jack of diamonds in the East hand. Assuming the finesse loses, declarer can then try to *drop the remaining diamond honor doubleton* before reverting to the heart finesse. Since a particular diamond honor singleton or doubleton is a better chance than the king singleton, starting diamonds from dummy gives declarer a better chance than starting hearts. There is also the additional chance that East will go up with the king of diamonds if he has it (so declarer should probably finesse against the jack of diamonds when he leads from dummy).

Note that it would be wrong to lead diamonds first from the South hand, for a losing diamond finesse and a heart return will force declarer to commit himself prematurely.

PROBLEM 19

Rubber bridge
North-South vulnerable
East-West 60 on score

NORTH
♠ 10 9 8
♡ J 2
◇ 7 6 5 4 3
♣ A K Q

SOUTH
♠ K Q J
♡ A Q
◇ A Q 10 2
♣ 5 4 3 2

SOUTH	WEST	NORTH	EAST
1 NT	Pass	3 NT	(All pass)

West leads the heart five, deuce, ten,?

Plan the play.

SOLUTION 19

♠ 10 9 8
♥ J 2
♦ 7 6 5 4 3
♣ A K Q

♠ 6 4
♥ K 9 7 5 4
♦ K J 8
♣ J 9 6

♠ A 7 5 3 2
♥ 10 8 6 3
♦ 9
♣ 10 8 7

♠ K Q J
♥ A Q
♦ A Q 10 2
♣ 5 4 3 2

To determine whether to attack diamonds or spades, declarer should first lead clubs. If clubs split 3-3, South can make certain of his contract by driving out the ace of spades. If clubs are not favorably split, South will need four diamond tricks and can attack that suit.

In order to provide for the contingency that he will need to attack diamonds, South should *cash the ace of diamonds at trick two*. This is a safety play that gives him the maximum chance to get four diamond tricks. It is essential to make this play at once, because there may be no further chance to reenter dummy after clubs are tested.

Cashing the ace of diamonds at trick two reduces South's chances of making *five* diamond tricks, but five diamond tricks will never be essential to the contract.

PROBLEM 20

Rubber bridge
Neither side vulnerable

NORTH
♠ 6 4
♡ K J 9 7
◇ 8 7 3
♣ 10 7 5 3

SOUTH
♠ A 5
♡ A Q 10 8
◇ A 6 5 2
♣ A K 6

SOUTH	WEST	NORTH	EAST
2 NT	Pass	3 ♣	Pass
3 ♡	Pass	4 ♡	(All pass)

West leads the spade jack, four, queen,?

Plan the play.

SOLUTION 20

```
            ♠ 6 4
            ♡ K J 9 7
            ◇ 8 7 3
            ♣ 10 7 5 3

♠ J 10 8                    ♠ K Q 9 7 3 2
♡ 6 2                       ♡ 5 4 3
◇ K J 10 9 4                ◇ Q
♣ 9 4 2                     ♣ Q J 8

            ♠ A 5
            ♡ A Q 10 8
            ◇ A 6 5 2
            ♣ A K 6
```

If the club honors do not drop doubleton, South's best chance is to find one minor split 3-3 and the other 4-2 or worse. He can then eliminate spades, draw trumps, play two rounds of one minor and three rounds of the other, hoping that the defender who wins the trick has to give him a ruff and discard. Clubs is the superior throw-in suit (because the defense is less likely to be able to unblock), so declarer should hope for unbalanced diamonds. The basic plan, therefore is to strip the majors, duck one diamond, then take the minor-suit tops and lead a third club.

Declarer must be careful, however, to *win the first spade*. He has nothing to lose by this—after drawing three trumps he plays back spades and proceeds as before. If the first spade is ducked, East may shift to a diamond. Declarer must now guess whether East holds one diamond or two.

PROBLEM 21

Rubber bridge
North-South vulnerable

NORTH
♠ 7
♡ 4 3
♢ A 10 7 6 5
♣ A K 8 3 2

SOUTH
♠ A K
♡ A K Q J 10 9
♢ 9 8 4 2
♣ 6

SOUTH	WEST	NORTH	EAST
1 ♡	Pass	2 ♢	Pass
4 NT	Pass	5 ♡	Pass
5 NT	Pass	6 ♢	Pass
6 ♡	(All Pass)		

West leads the spade jack.

Plan the play.

SOLUTION 21

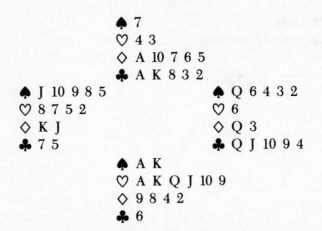

```
              ♠ 7
              ♡ 4 3
              ◇ A 10 7 6 5
              ♣ A K 8 3 2
♠ J 10 9 8 5                    ♠ Q 6 4 3 2
♡ 8 7 5 2                       ♡ 6
◇ K J                          ◇ Q 3
♣ 7 5                          ♣ Q J 10 9 4
              ♠ A K
              ♡ A K Q J 10 9
              ◇ 9 8 4 2
              ♣ 6
```

Declarer has two main chances: a 2-2 diamond split and a 4-3 club split. He should win the opening lead and cash one high trump. (If trumps split 5-0, there is little point playing on clubs.) If both opponents follow he should play the ace *and king* of clubs, then ruff a club. If clubs split 4-3, declarer ruffs a spade, ruffs a club, and claims his slam, using the ace of diamonds as entry to the long club.

If clubs split 5-2, declarer gives up on clubs, draws trumps, and ducks a diamond. This will bring in the contract if diamonds are 2-2 or if a squeeze can be developed.

The trap to avoid is ruffing a club before cashing the second honor in dummy. This gains only if clubs break 6-1 (and then probably only if West has the singleton) and loses in a fairly normal distribution of the cards such as the one shown. By playing correctly, declarer sees the club break in time to give up on clubs and play diamonds. If the key play is not made, and a second club is ruffed, declarer loses control and cannot take advantage of the 2-2 diamond break.

PROBLEM 22

Matchpoints
North-South vulnerable

> NORTH
> ♠ A K 7 3
> ♡ 9 6 4
> ◇ J 8 3
> ♣ A K 5
>
> SOUTH
> ♠ —
> ♡ Q 8 5
> ◇ A K 5 2
> ♣ Q J 9 7 6 4

SOUTH	WEST	NORTH	EAST
1 ♣	Pass	1 ♠	Pass
2 ♣	Pass	4 ♣	Pass
5 ♣	(All Pass)		

West leads the spade queen.

Plan the play.

SOLUTION 22

♠ A K 7 3
♡ 9 6 4
◇ J 8 3
♣ A K 5

♠ Q J 10 9   ♠ 8 6 5 4 2
♡ K 10 3   ♡ A J 7 2
◇ Q 10 9 6 4   ◇ 7
♣ 2   ♣ 10 8 3

♠ —
♡ Q 8 5
◇ A K 5 2
♣ Q J 9 7 6 4

After discarding two heart losers on the top spades, South must decide how to handle his diamonds. The surest shot is to plan to ruff the fourth diamond in dummy, so declarer plans to cash two diamonds and lead a third round, ruffing the fourth diamond in dummy if the suit does not divide well.

To avoid having his diamond honors ruffed if East is short in diamonds, South should lead towards them twice—the first time immediately after winning his two spades. Now South plans to use the club ace as the entry to lead towards his second diamond honor, but *should lead his remaining heart first*. If he fails to do this, East may ruff the second diamond and put West in with a heart to get a second diamond ruff.

After giving up his heart, South wins the return, leads a trump to dummy, leads up to his second diamond honor, and continues with his plan to ruff the fourth diamond.

PROBLEM 23

Rubber bridge
East-West vulnerable

> NORTH
> ♠ 10 9 8 4
> ♡ K J 2
> ◇ Q 9 3
> ♣ 4 3 2
>
> SOUTH
> ♠ A K Q J 6 3 2
> ♡ A 5 3
> ◇ —
> ♣ K 6 5

SOUTH	WEST	NORTH	EAST
—	—	Pass	Pass
4 ♠	(All pass)		

West leads the diamond king.

Plan the play.

♠ 10 9 8 4
♡ K J 2
◇ Q 9 3
♣ 4 3 2

♠ 7   ♠ 5
♡ 8 6 4   ♡ Q 10 9 7
◇ A K 10 6 4   ◇ J 8 7 5 2
♣ A 9 8 7   ♣ Q J 10

♠ A K Q J 6 3 2
♡ A 5 3
◇ —
♣ K 6 5

South can virtually assure his contract by discarding a *heart* on the first trick. He wins the return of, say, a trump, leads a second trump to dummy if necessary, ruffs the nine of diamonds, plays three rounds of hearts ruffing in his hand, leads another trump to dummy, and plays the queen of diamonds, discarding a club. West is end-played.

PROBLEM 24

Rubber bridge
East-West vulnerable

> NORTH
> ♠ 10 9 8 4
> ♡ K J 2
> ◇ Q 9 3
> ♣ 4 3 2
>
> SOUTH
> ♠ A K Q J 6 3
> ♡ A 5 3
> ◇ 5
> ♣ A Q 5

SOUTH	WEST	NORTH	EAST
—	—	Pass	Pass
1 ♠	Pass	1 NT	Pass
4 ♠	(All Pass)		

West leads the diamond king and shifts to a spade, East following.

Plan the play.

SOLUTION 24

```
              ♠ 10 9 8 4
              ♡ K J 2
              ◊ Q 9 3
              ♣ 4 3 2
♠ 7 2                            ♠ 5
♡ 10 9 7                         ♡ Q 8 6 4
◊ A K 10 6                       ◊ J 8 7 4 2
♣ K 9 8 7                        ♣ J 10 6
              ♠ A K Q J 6 3
              ♡ A 5 3
              ◊ 5
              ♣ A Q 5
```

The best play is to draw two trumps, ending in dummy, and lead the jack of hearts! If West has the queen of hearts he can win and return a heart, but declarer can use same throw in as in the previous problem.

If East has the queen of hearts and covers, South wins and leads a heart towards dummy. If West plays the highest outstanding heart, declarer ducks and the play proceeds as before. Otherwise declarer wins in dummy, ruffs a diamond, leads a trump to dummy, and plays the queen of diamonds, *discarding his last heart*.

If West started with no more than two hearts, he is endplayed. If West leads a heart and East does not beat it, South throws a club and West cannot escape. Thus, if West started with ♡ 10 9 8, ♡ 10 9 8 7, or five or more hearts, the contract will still come home.

Furthermore, if West holds ♡ 10 9 x (as in the diagram), he *still* cannot escape the end-play, even if he unblocks on the first round. And, of course, there are many Wests who would fail to unblock from an original holding of ♡ 10 x x.

Finally, there is always the club finesse if all else fails.

PROBLEM 25

Rubber bridge
North-South vulnerable

> NORTH
> ♠ K 5 4
> ♡ 8 2
> ◇ Q J 9 5
> ♣ A J 6 4
>
> SOUTH
> ♠ A J 10 3
> ♡ A J
> ◇ A K 10 4 2
> ♣ Q 2

SOUTH	WEST	NORTH	EAST
1 ◇	Pass	3 ◇	Pass
6 ◇	(All pass)		

West leads the king of hearts, won by South's ace. Declarer draws trumps, which break 2-2. How should South plan the play?

SOLUTION 25

♠ K 5 4
♥ 8 2
♦ Q J 9 5
♣ A J 6 4

♠ 6 2
♥ K Q 10 9 7
♦ 8 6
♣ 10 8 7 5

♠ Q 9 8 7
♥ 6 5 4 3
♦ 7 3
♣ K 9 3

♠ A J 10 3
♥ A J
♦ A K 10 4 2
♣ Q 2

If South is going to take the spade finesse, he should plan to take it through East—no matter how many spades East has, declarer can get four spade tricks and discard the losing heart from dummy. But before playing spades, declarer should lead the queen of clubs. West is not aware of South's problem, and it is a reasonable assumption that West will play the king of clubs if he has it.

If West covers, declarer is home: club ace and jack, club ruff, spade king, club ruff, heart jack end-playing West.

If West does not cover, South should assume East holds the king of clubs. He should go up with dummy's ace of clubs, cash the spade king, take a spade finesse, and, assuming this wins, go back to dummy with a trump for another spade finesse. Then he can discard dummy's heart on the fourth spade, and ruff his losing heart.

PROBLEM 26

Rubber bridge
Neither side vulnerable

> **NORTH**
> ♠ 10 6 4 2
> ♡ 8 5 4
> ◇ A Q 6
> ♣ 9 4 2
>
> **SOUTH**
> ♠ A J 9 8 7 5 3
> ♡ A K Q
> ◇ 8
> ♣ A Q

SOUTH	WEST	NORTH	EAST
2 ♣	Pass	2 ◇	Pass
2 ♠	Pass	3 ♠	Pass
4 ♣	Pass	4 ◇	Pass
6 ♠	(All pass)		

West leads the nine of hearts, and South wins. On the lead of the ace of spades, East discards a small heart. How should South plan the play?

SOLUTION 26

```
                    ♠ 10 6 4 2
                    ♡ 8 5 4
                    ◇ A Q 6
                    ♣ 9 4 2

  ♠ K Q                          ♠ —
  ♡ 9 2                          ♡ J 10 7 6 3
  ◇ J 5 4 3 2                    ◇ K 10 9 7
  ♣ J 6 5 3                      ♣ K 10 8 7

                    ♠ A J 9 8 7 5 3
                    ♡ A K Q
                    ◇ 8
                    ♣ A Q
```

It appears that declarer must guess whether to finesse in diamonds or in clubs. He can end-play West by cashing his high hearts and, if West refuses to ruff, leading a trump. But West will undoubtedly lead a diamond, forcing declarer to pick a minor-suit finesse.

Nor can declarer eliminate diamonds from both hands, as he is short an immediate entry to dummy.

Although there is no way of forcing a club lead from West, South can make the contract without a guess if *either* minor-suit king is on-side After winning the spade ace he should immediately *lead a diamond to the ace*, then run his hearts, then throw West in with a trump (if necessary). West must exit with a diamond and declarer can try to win dummy's queen *without risk*. If East shows up with the king of diamonds, declarer must resort to the club finesse—but two chances are better than one.

PROBLEM 27

Rubber bridge
Neither side vulnerable

NORTH
♠ K 6 4
♡ K J 9 5
♢ Q 10 2
♣ K J 4

SOUTH
♠ A Q 2
♡ A Q 10 4
♢ K 4 3
♣ A Q 10

SOUTH	WEST	NORTH	EAST
2 NT	Pass	3 ♣	Pass
3 ♡	Pass	6 ♡	(All pass)

West leads the jack of spades. South draws three rounds of trumps, and East throws a club on the third round.

Before starting diamonds, declarer clears the black suits. *In which hand should he take the final black-suit trick?* If East throws a club on the second spade, and West throws a spade on the third club, *how should South play the diamonds?*

SOLUTION 27

```
              ♠ K 6 4
              ♡ K J 9 5
              ◇ Q 10 2
              ♣ K J 4

♠ J 10 9 7 5 3              ♠ 8
♡ 6 3 2                     ♡ 8 7
◇ 7 5                       ◇ A J 9 8 6
♣ 8 7                       ♣ 9 6 5 3 2

              ♠ A Q 2
              ♡ A Q 10 4
              ◇ K 4 3
              ♣ A Q 10
```

South should be in his own hand after taking his black-suit tricks. In an elimination position it is as effective to lead the diamond king as to lead up to it. But South may want to lead *towards* dummy's queen of diamonds, rather than lead the queen itself (in case West has A x).

When the complete count becomes available, and West is known to hold a doubleton diamond, the best play in diamonds is to lead low to the queen, and, if East wins and returns a diamond, to duck it to dummy's ten. This wins in 16 cases out of a possible 21 (West has AJ, Ax, or xx) whereas leading the king wins in only 6 cases out of 21 (West has AJ or Jx).

Note that on a double-dummy basis the contract is defeated by a diamond lead, which prevents declarer from developing the end-position.

PROBLEM 28

Rubber bridge
Neither side vulnerable

NORTH
♠ J 5 3 2
♡ K 8 5
♢ Q 6 3
♣ Q 5 4

SOUTH
♠ A Q 8 6 4
♡ A 6
♢ A K 8
♣ A K 10

SOUTH	WEST	NORTH	EAST
2 ♣	Pass	2 ♢	Pass
2 ♠	Pass	3 ♠	Pass
3 NT	Pass	5 ♠	Pass
6 ♠	(All pass)		

West leads the queen of hearts. Obviously, South need only avoid losing two tricks in trumps. *What is the best line of play to achieve this?*

SOLUTION 28

♠ J 5 3 2
♡ K 8 5
◇ Q 6 3
♣ Q 5 4

♠ K 10 9 7
♡ Q J 10
◇ J 9 5
♣ 8 7 2

♠ —
♡ 9 7 4 3 2
◇ 10 7 4 2
♣ J 9 6 3

♠ A Q 8 6 4
♡ A 6
◇ A K 8
♣ A K 10

South should win the first lead in his hand and lead a spade towards dummy's jack. If both opponents follow, declarer will have no trouble unless the return is ruffed, which is very unlikely.

If West shows out on the first spade lead, declarer puts up dummy's jack and later double finesses against East's spades.

If East shows out on dummy's jack of spades, declarer must rely on a trump coup. This will succeed if West has exactly the same distribution as North. After winning dummy's spade jack, declarer plays the king of hearts, ruffs a heart, cashes all his minor-suit winners, and leads a low spade to end-play West.

PROBLEM 29

Rubber bridge
North-South vulnerable

> ### NORTH
> ♠ 6 5 4 3
> ♡ 8 4 3 2
> ◇ A J 10 6
> ♣ 6
>
> ### SOUTH
> ♠ A K 10 2
> ♡ A K Q
> ◇ K Q 5
> ♣ A K J

SOUTH	WEST	NORTH	EAST
2 ♣	Pass	2 ◇	Pass
2 ♠	Pass	3 ♠	Pass
4 ♣	Pass	4 ◇	Pass
4 ♡	Pass	4 ♠	Pass
6 NT	(All pass)		

West leads the deuce of diamonds.

What is the best play for declarer? Does this play guarantee the contract?

SOLUTION 29

```
            ♠ 6 5 4 3
            ♡ 8 4 3 2
            ◇ A J 10 6
            ♣ 6
♠ Q J 8 7                    ♠ 9
♡ J 9                        ♡ 10 7 6 5
◇ 7 4 3 2                    ◇ 9 8
♣ Q 10 8                     ♣ 9 7 5 4 3 2
            ♠ A K 10 2
            ♡ A K Q
            ◇ K Q 5
            ♣ A K J
```

The contract is guaranteed. South must play to keep East off lead (to avoid a club play).

Declarer should win the diamond ten in dummy and lead a spade. If East does not produce an honor, the spade ten will force West on lead. South now wins the diamond return in his hand, and plays one high spade and three high hearts. If these two suits are guarded by the same defender, declarer plays ace-king of clubs (throwing a spade from dummy), then runs diamonds to produce a spade-heart squeeze. If the majors are stopped in opposite hands (as in the diagram), South plays off his other high spades, then runs diamonds to produce a double squeeze (neither opponent can guard clubs).

If East plays a spade honor at trick two, South wins and returns a low spade. If East can win this trick, three spade tricks will be available; if West wins this trick, declarer proceeds as before.

PROBLEM 30

Rubber bridge
North-South vulnerable

NORTH
♠ Q J 6 3
♡ Q 5
◇ Q J 6 2
♣ 8 4 2

SOUTH
♠ A K
♡ A K
◇ A 5 3
♣ J 10 9 7 6 5

SOUTH	WEST	NORTH	EAST
1 ♣	Pass	1 ◇	Pass
2 NT	Pass	3 NT	(All pass)

West leads the jack of hearts. *What is the best play for the contract? What is the approximate chance of success of this play?*

♠ Q J 6 3
♡ Q 5
♢ Q J 6 2
♣ 8 4 2

♠ 10 8 7   ♠ 9 5 4 2
♡ J 10 9 8 6   ♡ 7 4 3 2
♢ K 9 7 4   ♢ 10 8
♣ 3   ♣ A K Q

♠ A K
♡ A K
♢ A 5 3
♣ J 10 9 7 6 5

South's best chance to untangle his tricks is to win the
first trick, take the two top spades, and then lead a low
diamond to dummy's jack.

If the diamond jack wins, declarer should discard his
remaining high heart on a spade honor, lead a diamond to
the ace and a third round of diamonds.

If East captures the diamond jack with the king, South
has an entry to dummy in diamonds and can try for a 3-3
diamond split.

This plans succeeds any time West has the diamond
king (50%) and also if East has exactly three diamonds to
the king (18%). These cases are exclusive of one another, so
the total chance is roughly 68%.

PROBLEM 31

Matchpoints
North-South vulnerable

                    NORTH
                    ♠ A K J 6
                    ♡ 5 4
                    ◇ 6 4 3
                    ♣ 8 4 3 2

                    SOUTH
                    ♠ 8 7
                    ♡ A K Q
                    ◇ A K Q J
                    ♣ A K 6 5

SOUTH	WEST	NORTH	EAST
—	3 ♡	Pass	Pass
4 NT	Pass	6 NT	All pass

West leads the queen of clubs. South wins with the ace and plays the king of clubs, on which East discards a small spade. South now tests two rounds of diamonds, West throwing a heart on the second round, and three rounds of hearts. East discards two diamonds. South can now make certain of his contract.

How?

SOLUTION 31

```
              ♠ A K J 6
              ♡ 5 4
              ◇ 6 4 3
              ♣ 8 4 3 2
♠ 2                          ♠ Q 10 9 5 4 3
♡ J 10 9 8 7 6 2            ♡ 3
◇ 5                          ◇ 10 9 8 7 2
♣ Q J 10 9                   ♣ 7
              ♠ 8 7
              ♡ A K Q
              ◇ A K Q J
              ♣ A K 6 5
```

As West started with seven hearts, four clubs, and one diamond, he has one (unknown) spade. South leads a spade to the ace and finds out what that card is, then cashes his diamonds.

(a) If West's thirteenth card was the nine or ten of spades, South leads his remaining spade to dummy's jack, end-playing East.

(b) If West's unknown card was a low spade (as in the diagram), this position will be reached as South leads his last diamond:

NORTH
♠ K J 6

WEST   **EAST**
Immaterial   ♠ Q 10 9 5

SOUTH
♠ 7

East is squeezed in spades. (South knows East's exact holding: If East throws the spade five, South passes the seven; otherwise, South leads to the jack.)

PROBLEM 32

Rubber bridge
Both sides vulnerable

NORTH
♠ 10
♡ A K 10
♢ A 6 2
♣ K J 10 9 6 4

SOUTH
♠ A K Q J 8 4 2
♡ 8 2
♢ K J 5 3
♣ —

SOUTH	WEST	NORTH	EAST
1 ♠	Pass	2 ♣	Pass
2 ♢	Pass	2 ♡	Pass
4 ♠	Pass	4 NT	Pass
5 ♢	Pass	6 ♠	(All pass)

West leads the heart jack to dummy's ace. The jack of clubs is led from dummy, ruffed when East follows small. Both defenders follow when a spade is led to the ten, and East shows out when a low club is led from dummy. South can now make certain of his contract.

How?

SOLUTION 32

♠ 10
♡ A K 10
♢ A 6 2
♣ K J 10 9 6 4

♠ 3   ♠ 9 7 6 5
♡ J 6   ♡ Q 9 7 5 4 3
♢ Q 10 9 4   ♢ 8 7
♣ A Q 8 7 5 3   ♣ 2

♠ A K Q J 8 4 2
♡ 8 2
♢ K J 5 3
♣ —

After ruffing the club, South plays two more trumps:

NORTH
♠ —
♡ A 10
♢ A 6 2
♣ 10 9

SOUTH
♠ A K
♡ 8
♢ K J 5 3
♣ —

On the lead of the spade king, West must keep two clubs (or a club trick can be established by ruffing) and four red cards. North now discards the club nine. South leads a heart to dummy's ace. If West follows (or throws a diamond), he can have at most three diamonds left, so king, ace, and another diamond will clear the suit. If West throws a club under the ace of hearts, he can be thrown in' with a club and forced to lead up to South's diamond holding.

PROBLEM 33

Rubber bridge
North-South vulnerable

NORTH
♠ 5 2
♡ K 6 4 3 2
♢ J 8 7 5 4
♣ 9

SOUTH
♠ A K Q 7 6 3
♡ A Q 5
♢ A Q 10
♣ A

SOUTH	WEST	NORTH	EAST
2 ♣	3 ♣	Pass	5 ♣
5 ♠	Pass	6 ♠	Pass
Pass	Pass		

West leads the club king and East plays the deuce. South plays two top spades and West discards a club.

How should South play?

SOLUTION 33

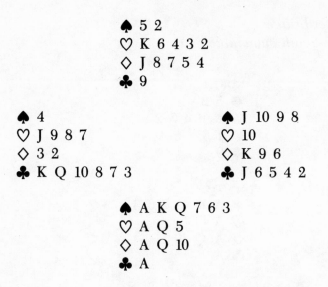

♠ 5 2
♡ K 6 4 3 2
♢ J 8 7 5 4
♣ 9

♠ 4
♡ J 9 8 7
♢ 3 2
♣ K Q 10 8 7 3

♠ J 10 9 8
♡ 10
♢ K 9 6
♣ J 6 5 4 2

♠ A K Q 7 6 3
♡ A Q 5
♢ A Q 10
♣ A

South should *not* lead queen and another trump. If he does, East may return a diamond and declarer will be forced to guess.

Instead, South should try the ace-queen of hearts after the third high trump. If hearts break 3-2, South gives up a trump trick, and otherwise finesses diamonds.

PROBLEM 34

IMP scoring
North-South vulnerable

NORTH
♠ 6 4 2
♡ A 9 5 2
♢ 9
♣ 6 5 4 3 2

SOUTH
♠ A K Q 7 5 3
♡ 6
♢ A J 4
♣ A K 8

SOUTH	WEST	NORTH	EAST
2 ♣	Pass	2 ♢	Pass
2 ♠	Pass	3 ♠	Pass
6 ♠	Pass	Pass	Pass

West leads the heart three.

Plan the play.

SOLUTION 34

```
              ♠ 6 4 2
              ♡ A 9 5 2
              ◇ 9
              ♣ 6 5 4 3 2

♠ J 10 9 8                    ♠ —
♡ K J 8 3                     ♡ Q 10 7 4
◇ Q 6 2                       ◇ K 10 8 7 5 3
♣ J 9                         ♣ Q 10 7

              ♠ A K Q 7 5 3
              ♡ 6
              ◇ A J 4
              ♣ A K 8
```

After winning the heart ace on the first trick, South should ruff a heart (safe, on East's failure to bid). The purpose of this play is to prepare for a possible 4-0 trump division—the only serious danger to the contract. Now a round of trumps. If trumps are not 4-0, declarer ruffs two diamonds in dummy (returning to his hand is fairly safe).

If East turns up with four trumps, South should cash the ace and king of clubs and crossruff in the red suits, hoping to combine his club and trump losers.

Things are tougher if West shows up with all four trumps. Now South can succeed only if West has exactly 4-4-3-2 distribution, once again by cashing the top clubs and crossruffing.

PROBLEM 35

Rubber bridge
Neither side vulnerable

NORTH
♠ K J 9 5 4
♡ 10 6 4 2
♢ A Q
♣ 7 5

SOUTH
♠ A Q 10 8 6 2
♡ A K
♢ 10 6
♣ A Q 3

SOUTH	WEST	NORTH	EAST
1 ♠	Pass	3 ♠	Pass
6 ♠	Pass	Pass	Pass

West leads the diamond five.

How should South play?

SOLUTION 35

♠ K J 9 5 4
♡ 10 6 4 2
◇ A Q
♣ 7 5

♠ 3
♡ 9 7 5 3
◇ J 8 7 5 4
♣ K 10 2

♠ 7
♡ Q J 8
◇ K 9 3 2
♣ J 9 8 6 4

♠ A Q 10 8 6 2
♡ A K
◇ 10 6
♣ A Q 3

The best play for seven is to take both minor-suit finesses. However, if declarer is willing to reduce his chances for the overtrick, he can also try to drop the queen-jack of hearts doubleton or tripleton. In rubber bridge, therefore, the best play is to go up with the ace of diamonds, draw trumps, cash the ace-king of hearts, enter dummy with a trump, and ruff a heart.

If the ten of hearts is not established, dummy can be entered with a third round of trumps in order to ruff the last heart. (If trumps were 2-0, South would cash the heart ace-king *before* taking the second trump.) South now leads to the queen of diamonds. If West has the diamond king (so that the diamond finesse would have won), he is end-played. If East has the diamond king, declarer must fall back on the club finesse.

PROBLEM 36

Rubber bridge
East-West vulnerable

NORTH
♠ J 7 5 3
♡ 4 3 2
♢ 8 5
♣ J 4 3 2

SOUTH
♠ A K Q 8 6 4 2
♡ —
♢ A Q
♣ A 10 9 8

SOUTH	WEST	NORTH	EAST
2 ♣	Pass	2 ♢	Pass
2 ♠	Pass	2 NT	Pass
3 ♣	Pass	4 ♠	Pass
6 ♠	Pass	Pass	Pass

West leads the heart king.

Plan the play.

SOLUTION 36

```
                 ♠ J 7 5 3
                 ♡ 4 3 2
                 ◇ 8 5
                 ♣ J 4 3 2

 ♠ 9                        ♠ 10
 ♡ K Q 10 7 5               ♡ A J 9 8 6
 ◇ K 10 7 4 3 2             ◇ J 9 6
 ♣ K                        ♣ Q 7 6 5

                 ♠ A K Q 8 6 4 2
                 ♡ —
                 ◇ A Q
                 ♣ A 10 9 8
```

South should ruff the opening lead high and lead the
eight of spades to the jack. If trumps break 2-0, he should
take an immediate diamond finesse (which he must assume will win), then use his two trump entries to dummy
to take two club finesses (leading low to the eight the first
time and leading the jack through the second time).

If trumps break 1-1, however, declarer can avoid the
risk of the diamond finesse when West has a singleton
club honor. He should ruff a heart high, lead the six of
spades to the seven, ruff dummy's last heart high, and
lead the four of spades to the five. Now a low club to the
ten will endplay West if, as in the diagram, he began with
a singleton club honor. If West can exit with a club,
declarer picks up the clubs and later tries the diamond
finesse. If the club ten holds, declarer leads a low club.

PROBLEM 37

Matchpoints
East-West vulnerable

NORTH
♠ K 3 2
♡ A Q 5 4
♢ 8 6 3 2
♣ 6 5

SOUTH
♠ A Q J 10 8
♡ K J
♢ 5
♣ A K Q 4 3

SOUTH	WEST	NORTH	EAST
2 ♣	5 ♢	Pass	Pass
5 ♠	Pass	6 ♠	(All pass)

West leads the diamond king to East's ace. East returns the spade seven, South winning with the queen as West sheds a diamond. Assuming East has no more diamonds, *how does South insure his contract?*

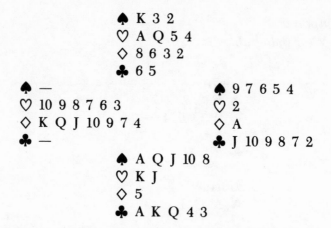

♠ K 3 2
♡ A Q 5 4
◇ 8 6 3 2
♣ 6 5

♠ —
♡ 10 9 8 7 6 3
◇ K Q J 10 9 7 4
♣ —

♠ 9 7 6 5 4
♡ 2
◇ A
♣ J 10 9 8 7 2

♠ A Q J 10 8
♡ K J
◇ 5
♣ A K Q 4 3

Obviously, West has wild distribution, even aside from his seven diamonds. But does he have a lot of hearts (in which case South can ruff a club in dummy), or a lot of clubs (in which case South can simply cash his four heart tricks)? South cannot with certainty draw trumps to squeeze West in diamonds and his other long suit because South does not know which that long suit is, and will not know how to continue after the fifth trump.

Nonetheless, the contract is guaranteed. South first cashes the heart king. East must follow, else West has 14 cards. If West shows out, South takes the heart jack, spade king, two hearts, then draws trumps. If West follows to the heart king, East must hold at least one club, so South cashes the club ace without risk. If West shows out (see diagram), declarer ruffs a club high in dummy, finesses the spade eight and claims. If West follows to the club ace, it must be safe for South to cash the heart jack. If West shows out, South proceeds as before. If West follows to the heart jack, the second club must go through. Now, a club is ruffed with the king of spades, and declarer draws trumps and claims.

PROBLEM 38

Rubber bridge
North-South vulnerable

NORTH
♠ A 10 2
♡ 6 4 3 2
♢ 4 2
♣ K Q J 3

SOUTH
♠ K Q J
♡ A 8 7 5
♢ A K Q J 10 5
♣ —

SOUTH	WEST	NORTH	EAST
1 ♢	Pass	1 ♡	Pass
2 ♠	Pass	2 NT	Pass
4 ♡	Pass	4 ♠	Pass
6 ♢	Pass	Pass	Pass

West leads the eight of spades.

How should South plan the play?

SOLUTION 38

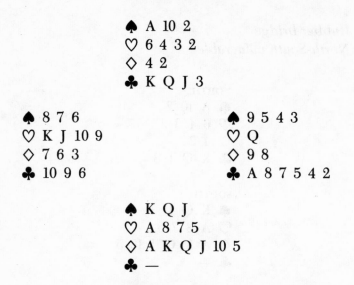

♠ A 10 2
♡ 6 4 3 2
◇ 4 2
♣ K Q J 3

♠ 8 7 6
♡ K J 10 9
◇ 7 6 3
♣ 10 9 6

♠ 9 5 4 3
♡ Q
◇ 9 8
♣ A 8 7 5 4 2

♠ K Q J
♡ A 8 7 5
◇ A K Q J 10 5
♣ —

There is only one reasonable chance for the contract, so declarer might as well play for it. The hearts must break 4-1 (or 5-0) and the defender short in hearts must hold the club ace.

To take advantage of this (admittedly slim) possibility, South should win the opening lead in his own hand, draw trumps, cash the heart ace, lead a spade to the ace, and lead the king of clubs from dummy. On this, he discards his remaining (blocking) spade whether or not East plays the ace. If the defender with the ace of clubs has no more hearts, he must give dummy three black-suit tricks, to account for declarer's three losing hearts.

PROBLEM 39

Rubber bridge
East-West vulnerable

NORTH
♠ A 10 2
♡ 6 4 3 2
♢ 4 2
♣ K J 3 2

SOUTH
♠ K Q J
♡ A K 7 5
♢ A K Q J 10 5
♣ —

SOUTH	WEST	NORTH	EAST
1 ♢	Pass	1 ♡	Pass
2 ♠	Pass	2 NT	Pass
5 ♡	Pass	5 NT	Pass
6 ♢	Pass	Pass	Pass

West leads the spade eight.

Plan the play.

♠ A 10 2
♡ 6 4 3 2
◇ 4 2
♣ K J 3 2

♠ 8 7 6	♠ 9 5 4 3
♡ Q 10 9 8	♡ J
◇ 7 6 3	◇ 9 8
♣ A 10 6	♣ Q 9 8 7 5 4

SOUTH
♠ K Q J
♡ A K 7 5
◇ A K Q J 10 5
♣ —

There will be no difficulty if hearts break 3-2. If not, the most likely chance is that the defender with long hearts will also hold the ace of clubs (and can therefore be subjected to a squeeze).

Accordingly, South should win the spade lead in his hand, draw trumps, and lead a low heart. He should win any return in his hand and lead out the rest of his trumps, then cash spades ending in dummy. If either defender began with four or more hearts and the ace of clubs, he will be squeezed.

Note that if South cashes one high heart before conceding a heart, the defense can play a third round of hearts and destroy the necessary entry for the squeeze.

PROBLEM 40

Rubber bridge
Neither side vulnerable

        NORTH
        ♠ K 10 3 2
        ♡ K Q 10
        ◇ A 10 5 2
        ♣ 6 4

        SOUTH
        ♠ 6
        ♡ A J 9 8 7
        ◇ J 4 3
        ♣ A K 8 2

SOUTH	WEST	NORTH	EAST
1 ♡	Pass	1 ♠	Pass
2 ♣	Pass	3 ♡	Pass
4 ♡	(All pass)		

West leads the heart three; East plays the five.

Plan the play.

SOLUTION 40

♠ K 10 3 2
♡ K Q 10
♢ A 10 5 2
♣ 6 4

♠ Q 8 7 5 4   ♠ A J 9
♡ 4 3 2   ♡ 6 5
♢ 9 8 7   ♢ K Q 6
♣ J 5   ♣ Q 10 9 7 3

♠ 6
♡ A J 9 8 7
♢ J 4 3
♣ A K 8 2

After winning the opening lead, declarer should cash the ace-king of clubs, ruff a club in dummy, and draw trumps. Assuming a high club was not ruffed, trumps are 3-2, and clubs are 4-3, South now leads his last club. If East wins this trick, he is end-played. If West wins and leads a diamond, declarer ducks: if West leads a spade declarer covers his card. In either case, East is end-played.

If West began with five clubs, declarer, after drawing trumps, leads a spade and covers West's card, end-playing East. If East began with five clubs declarer, after drawing trumps, leads his last club. East does best to win and lead his last club, in which case declarer discards a spade, end-playing East (if East leads a low spade, South pitches a diamond).

If trumps break 4-1 South discovers this in time to adopt a more straightforward plan for setting up his tenth trick.

PROBLEM 41

Rubber bridge
Both sides vulnerable

NORTH
♠ A 8 6 2
♡ A
♢ K 8 5 2
♣ A J 4 2

SOUTH
♠ K 9 5 4
♡ —
♢ A Q 7 6 4 3
♣ K 8 7

SOUTH	WEST	NORTH	EAST
—	—	1 ♣	Pass
1 ♢	Pass	3 ♢	Pass
6 ♢	(All Pass)		

West leads the diamond jack and East shows out.

How can South make certain of his contract?

SOLUTION 41

                    ♠ A 8 6 2
                    ♡ A
                    ◇ K 8 5 2
                    ♣ A J 4 2

    ♠ Q J 10 7   ♠ 3
    ♡ K J 10 9   ♡ Q 8 7 6 5 4 3 2
    ◇ J 10 9   ◇ —
    ♣ 6 3   ♣ Q 10 9 5

                    ♠ K 9 5 4
                    ♡ —
                    ◇ A Q 7 6 4 3
                    ♣ K 8 7

Declarer should draw three rounds of trumps ending in
dummy, cash the ace of hearts for a club discard, lead a
club to the king, and play a spade towards dummy.

If West plays an honor, declarer can take the spade and
club aces and lead a spade to the nine. West is end-played:
if he plays a spade declarer will have no further loser in
the suit, and if he plays a club, a trick will be established in
dummy.

If West plays the three or seven of spades, declarer can
finesse dummy's eight, end-playing East. A club lead will
give declarer the needed discard, and a spade lead will
destroy East's remaining stopper in that suit (if any).

PROBLEM 42

Rubber bridge
Both sides vulnerable

NORTH
♠ A 10 6 2
♡ A
♢ K 8 5 2
♣ A 6 4 2

SOUTH
♠ K 7 5 4
♡ —
♢ A Q 7 6 4 3
♣ K J 8

SOUTH	WEST	NORTH	EAST
—	—	1 ♣	Pass
1 ♢	Pass	3 ♢	Pass
6 ♢	(All Pass)		

West leads the diamond jack and East follows. *How can South make certain of his contract?*

♠ A 10 6 2
♡ A
◇ K 8 5 2
♣ A 6 4 2

♠ 3	♠ Q J 9 8
♡ J 9 7 5 3 2	♡ K Q 10 8 6 4
◇ J 10	◇ 9
♣ Q 10 7 5	♣ 9 3

♠ K 7 5 4
♡ —
◇ A Q 7 6 4 3
♣ K J 8

Declarer should draw two trumps ending in dummy, cash the ace of hearts for a spade discard, lead a spade to the king, and play a spade towards dummy.

If West plays an honor declarer wins with dummy's ace and can later lead towards dummy's spade ten to produce a discard for his losing club.

If West plays a small spade on the second round, declarer picks up the suit with one loser by finessing dummy's ten.

If West shows out on the second spade, declarer wins with dummy's ace and leads a club, just covering whatever card East plays. If West wins he is endplayed and must give declarer a ruff-sluff or lead into a club tenace, either of which will allow declarer to dispose of his remaining losing spade.

PROBLEM 43

Rubber bridge
Both sides vulnerable

NORTH
♠ A K Q 2
♡ K J 4
♢ Q 9 7 5 2
♣ 3

SOUTH
♠ J 10 9
♡ A 8 2
♢ A 8 6
♣ A 10 9 7

SOUTH	WEST	NORTH	EAST
—	—	1 ♢	Pass
2 NT	Pass	3 NT	(All Pass)

West leads the spade eight. *What is the best play for nine tricks?*

SOLUTION 43

♠ A K Q 2
♡ K J 4
♢ Q 9 7 5 2
♣ 3

♠ 8 7 6 5   ♠ 4 3
♡ 10 7 5 3   ♡ Q 9 6
♢ 10   ♢ K J 4 3
♣ Q J 8 2   ♣ K 6 5 4

♠ J 10 9
♡ A 8 2
♢ A 8 6
♣ A 10 9 7

The main danger is that East will win an early diamond trick and attack clubs. If so, the defense may be able to build up three club tricks if West has two honors plus the eight.

Accordingly, South should win the opening lead in dummy and lead a low diamond, intending to finesse the eight. If this forces West on lead (as in the diagram), declarer can win the club return, enter dummy, and lead another diamond, intending to finesse the six as a safety play.

If East plays a diamond honor at trick two, and later wins his side's first diamond trick, declarer has available a wide choice of plays.

PROBLEM 44

Rubber bridge
Both sides vulnerable

> NORTH
> ♠ 6
> ♡ K Q 6 2
> ◇ K 8 4 3
> ♣ K J 9 6
>
> SOUTH
> ♠ A K 10
> ♡ J 4
> ◇ Q 9 6 2
> ♣ A Q 10 4

SOUTH	WEST	NORTH	EAST
—	—	1 ♡	Pass
2 NT	Pass	3 NT	(All Pass)

West leads the spade five, East playing the jack.

How can South ensure his contract?

```
              ♠ 6
              ♡ K Q 6 2
              ◇ K 8 4 3
              ♣ K J 9 6

♠ Q 9 8 5 3                    ♠ J 7 4 2
♡ 8 5 3                        ♡ A 10 9 7
◇ 5                            ◇ A J 10 7
♣ 8 7 5 3                      ♣ 2

              ♠ A K 10
              ♡ J 4
              ◇ Q 9 6 2
              ♣ A Q 10 4
```

Declarer should win the opening lead, enter dummy with a club, and lead a low heart. If East plays the ace, South has nine tricks. If West captures the jack with the ace, he cannot profitably lead spades, and South has enough time to get his ninth trick in diamonds.

If the heart jack wins, declarer should again enter dummy with a club and lead a low diamond. If East plays the ace, South has nine tricks. If the diamond queen wins, South shifts back to hearts for trick nine. If West takes the diamond queen with the ace, the only troublesome return he can make is a low diamond. If this occurs, South ducks in dummy, assuring two diamond tricks and his contract.

PROBLEM 45

Rubber bridge
East-West vulnerable

NORTH
♠ A 5 3 2
♡ A 8 6 4 3
◇ Q J
♣ A Q

SOUTH
♠ K J 10 9 8 4
♡ K Q 7 2
◇ A
♣ K J

SOUTH	WEST	NORTH	EAST
—	—	1 ♡	Pass
2 ♠	Pass	3 ♠	Pass
4 NT	Pass	5 ♠	Pass
6 ♣	Pass	6 ♠	(All pass)

West leads the ten of clubs. South can make virtually certain of his contract. *How?*

SOLUTION 45

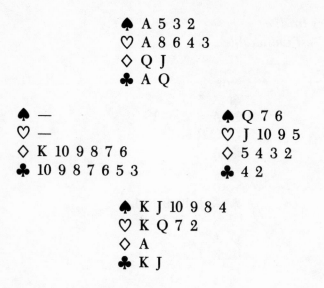

♠ A 5 3 2
♡ A 8 6 4 3
♢ Q J
♣ A Q

♠ —
♡ —
♢ K 10 9 8 7 6
♣ 10 9 8 7 6 5 3

♠ Q 7 6
♡ J 10 9 5
♢ 5 4 3 2
♣ 4 2

♠ K J 10 9 8 4
♡ K Q 7 2
♢ A
♣ K J

Assuming South misguesses spades and finds a 3-0 split, the only danger to the contract is a 4-0 heart split. Except in the unlikely event that South cannot eliminate the minors before a defender ruffs, there will be an easy endplay if the hearts and spades are held in opposite hands.

The correct play, therefore, is first to lead the spade king from the South hand. Even if East holds both majors, the contract is probably home (club ace, spade king, diamond ace, spade ace, diamond ruff, club, spade, and East is end-played). If South plays the spade ace first, he is doomed if West holds both majors. *West* can afford to lead a heart from J 10 9 5; East can't.

PROBLEM 46

Variable conditions
Both sides vulnerable

NORTH
♠ 8 4 3
♡ 9 2
◇ 9 4 3 2
♣ K 10 3 2

SOUTH
♠ A
♡ A K
◇ K Q 6 5
♣ A Q J 9 8 6

SOUTH	WEST	NORTH	EAST
2 ♣	Pass	2 ◇	Pass
3 ♣	Pass	4 ♣	Pass
4 ◇	Pass	5 ♣	(All pass)

West leads a trump and East follows. *How should South play (a) at rubber bridge, (b) at matchpoints?*

SOLUTION 46

```
              ♠ 8 4 3
              ♡ 9 2
              ◇ 9 4 3 2
              ♣ K 10 3 2
♠ Q 7 5 2                      ♠ K J 10 9 6
♡ Q 6 5 4                      ♡ J 10 8 7 3
◇ A J 10 8                     ◇ 7
♣ 4                            ♣ 7 5
              ♠ A
              ♡ A K
              ◇ K Q 6 5
              ♣ A Q J 9 8 6
```

At rubber bridge, South should take as few risks as possible. He should win the club queen and play the spade ace. If this is not ruffed, the contract is assured: club to dummy's ten, spade ruff, club to dummy's king, spade ruff, heart ace-king, diamond queen. If the diamond queen holds, South plays a low diamond next. If the diamond queen is captured by East, South ducks the diamond return; if West takes the diamond queen and leads low, dummy plays the nine.

At matchpoints, South cannot afford the luxury of the safety play. He needs the overtrick (easy to get if East has A x, A x x, or J 10 of diamonds) to beat pairs in three no-trump and five diamonds. So dummy's two club entries should be used to lead twice towards the king-queen of diamonds. South needn't worry about the pairs in six clubs—they will presumably go down two if he goes down one.

PROBLEM 47

IMP scoring
North-South vulnerable

NORTH
♠ A 6 5 2
♡ Q 10 6 5 3
♢ A K
♣ K 6

SOUTH
♠ K Q J 7
♡ 8 2
♢ J 8 6 5 4 3
♣ 9

SOUTH	WEST	NORTH	EAST
Pass	Pass	1 ♡	Pass
1 ♠	Pass	3 ♠	Pass
4 ♠	(All pass)		

West leads the spade three.

Plan the play.

SOLUTION 47

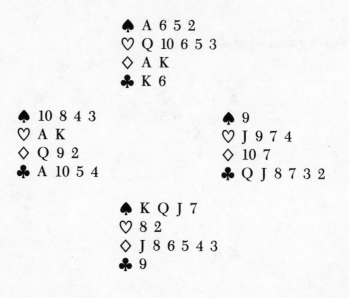

♠ A 6 5 2
♡ Q 10 6 5 3
◇ A K
♣ K 6

♠ 10 8 4 3
♡ A K
◇ Q 9 2
♣ A 10 5 4

♠ 9
♡ J 9 7 4
◇ 10 7
♣ Q J 8 7 3 2

♠ K Q J 7
♡ 8 2
◇ J 8 6 5 4 3
♣ 9

There is no hope if South needs two ruffs to establish his diamonds. If only one ruff is needed, however, South can guard against a 4-1 trump break with the defender long in diamonds having four trumps. To do this he must take care to win the first trick in dummy with the ace of spades. Then, ace-king of diamonds and, if the queen has not fallen, a spade to the king.

If spades are 3-2, South draws the last trump and claims his contract. If spades are 4-1, South leads a diamond. If, as in the diagram, one defender holds four spades and three diamonds, the contract will still be made. Be sure to note that this cannot be accomplished if the first trick is taken in the closed hand—declarer lacks entries and will lose control.

PROBLEM 48

Rubber bridge
Neither side vulnerable

NORTH
♠ Q J 6 4
♡ A 2
♢ K J 9 2
♣ J 10 4

SOUTH
♠ K 3
♡ K 5
♢ A Q 10 8 4 3
♣ A Q 6

SOUTH	WEST	NORTH	EAST
1 ♢	Pass	3 ♢	Pass
4 NT	Pass	5 ♢	Pass
6 ♢	(All pass)		

West leads the heart ten.

Plan the play.

SOLUTION 48

```
                    ♠ Q J 6 4
                    ♡ A 2
                    ◇ K J 9 2
                    ♣ J 10 4
♠ A 8                               ♠ 10 9 7 5 2
♡ 10 9 8 6 3                        ♡ Q J 7 4
◇ 7 6                               ◇ 5
♣ K 8 3 2                           ♣ 9 7 5
                    ♠ K 3
                    ♡ K 5
                    ◇ A Q 10 8 4 3
                    ♣ A Q 6
```

If South is to avoid the club finesse, he will probably
need to find one opponent with the singleton or doubleton ace of spades. The information content of the
opening lead is neutral (West holds the ten and nine of
hearts, East the queen and jack), so South should make his
choice depending on the distribution of the trump suit.

If East is (relatively) long in trumps, declarer should
play him for short spades by leading a spade to his king
and ducking a spade on the way back. If West is long in
trumps, as in the diagram, South should start spades by
leading low from his hand towards dummy's queen. If
this holds, he should cash off the other heart and lead to
the spade king, endplaying West if that defender started
with the doubleton ace of spades.

There is one other possibility, however. By leading a
spade to the king and a spade back after eliminating
hearts and diamonds, declarer triumphs if West started
with any of these spade holdings: A, 10-9, or 10-x where he
fails to unblock, in addition to five spades without the ace.
We leave to arithmeticians the problem of whether this
does or does not overcome the distributional inference of
West holding two out of the three trumps. We think not.

PROBLEM 49

Variable conditions
Both sides vulnerable

NORTH
♠ K 4 3
♡ 8 6 4 2
♢ A K Q 10 6
♣ A

SOUTH
♠ A J 10 9 8
♡ A K
♢ J 3
♣ 8 4 3 2

SOUTH	WEST	NORTH	EAST
1 ♠	Pass	3 ♢	Pass
3 ♠	Pass	4 ♣	Pass
4 ♡	Pass	6 ♠	(All pass)

Club king, *ace*, six, three. Spade three, deuce, *jack*, five. *Plan the play* (a) at rubber bridge; (b) at match-points.

SOLUTION 49

♠ K 4 3
♡ 8 6 4 2
◇ A K Q 10 6
♣ A

♠ Q 7 6 5   ♠ 2
♡ J 5 3   ♡ Q 10 9 7
◇ 9 8   ◇ 7 5 4 2
♣ K Q 10 5   ♣ J 9 7 6

♠ A J 10 9 8
♡ A K
◇ J 3
♣ 8 4 3 2

At rubber bridge, South should finesse spades back the other way! This guards against a clever hold-up by a West with four spades to the queen and short diamonds, and loses only if the opponents can obtain a red-suit ruff.

At matchpoints, South cannot afford this safety play. The contract is fairly normal and an overtrick seems likely. If West has made the hold-up play, he deserves to collect. In any event, declarer is not necessarily down after leading a spade to the king—West may have three or more diamonds.

An alternative matchpoint maneuver would be to lead a diamond to dummy and a spade, intending to finesse the ten. This risks probably unnecessary complications, however, if diamonds break 5-1.

PROBLEM 50

Rubber bridge
East-West vulnerable

NORTH
♠ K 5
♡ A K J
♢ 8 5 4 3 2
♣ K J 2

SOUTH
♠ A 8 4
♡ 4 3 2
♢ A K Q 7
♣ A 10 3

SOUTH	WEST	NORTH	EAST
1 NT	Pass	4 NT	Pass
5 ♢	(All pass)		

West leads the spade jack.

Plan the play.

SOLUTION 50

```
                    ♠ K 5
                    ♡ A K J
                    ◇ 8 5 4 3 2
                    ♣ K J 2

♠ J 10 9 3                        ♠ Q 7 6 2
♡ 8 7 6 5                         ♡ Q 10 9
◇ —                              ◇ J 10 9 6
♣ 9 8 7 6 5                       ♣ Q 4

                    ♠ A 8 4
                    ♡ 4 3 2
                    ◇ A K Q 7
                    ♣ A 10 3
```

Declarer should win the first trick in dummy and lead a diamond, intending to finesse the seven if East follows with the six. If this wins, the rest is easy. If West captures the seven, South can later draw trumps, ruff a spade in dummy, and play three rounds of hearts, end-playing the defense. In other words, South should not let his partner's failure to bid six diamonds stop him from making the best play for five.

Is this a safety play against only a 1-in-20 chance? (The chance of a 4-0 break is roughly 10%, so East will have all four trumps only about 5% of the time.) No, the danger is as great as 1-in-10. Assuming East would play the diamond six whenever he held it, half the originally possible diamond combinations (those in which West holds the six) become impossible, so the chance of East holding all four diamonds is roughly 5% out of 50%, or 1-in-10.

PROBLEM 51

Rubber bridge
Both sides vulnerable

NORTH
♠ A K 6 5 3
♡ J 9 4 2
◇ 2
♣ J 5 3

SOUTH
♠ Q 4 2
♡ A Q
◇ A K Q 5
♣ K 8 4 2

SOUTH	WEST	NORTH	EAST
2 NT	Pass	3 ♣	Pass
3 ◇	Pass	3 NT	(All pass)

West leads the diamond jack.

Plan the play.

SOLUTION 51

♠ A K 6 5 3
♡ J 9 4 2
◇ 2
♣ J 5 3

♠ 7   ♠ J 10 9 8
♡ K 6 3   ♡ 10 8 7 5
◇ J 10 9 8 6   ◇ 7 4 3
♣ A Q 10 9   ♣ 7 6

♠ Q 4 2
♡ A Q
◇ A K Q 5
♣ K 8 4 2

South should win the first trick and lead the heart queen. If the opponents win, they cannot attack clubs without giving declarer his ninth trick. Thus, there will be time to duck a spade and try for 3-2 or 4-1 spades, or the heart ten dropping, or the club ace onside. If the heart queen holds, declarer can duck a spade and retain similar chances.

Other plays do not cover so many possible lies of the opponents' cards. If, for example, declarer plays ace and queen of hearts, West may win and lead a third round of the suit. If this sets up a second defensive heart trick, declarer will have to guess whether to play on spades or clubs. Alternatively, if a spade is ducked at once, the clever defense of an immediate spade return will give declarer serious entry problems, and once again he may be at the mercy of the club position.

PROBLEM 52

Rubber bridge
North-South vulnerable

NORTH
♠ 9 5 2
♡ 8 4
♢ K 10 8
♣ A K J 9 6

SOUTH
♠ A Q 8
♡ —
♢ A Q J 9 6 4 3 2
♣ 7 2

SOUTH	WEST	NORTH	EAST
2 ♢	Pass	3 ♣	Pass
3 ♢	Pass	6 ♢	(All pass)

West leads a·trump; East follows.

What is the best play for the contract? Is the slam certain?

♠ 9 5 2
♡ 8 4
♢ K 10 8
♣ A K J 9 6

♠ K J 7 6 3   ♠ 10 4
♡ Q 9 7 5 3 2   ♡ A K J 10 6
♢ 7   ♢ 5
♣ 5   ♣ Q 10 8 4 3

♠ A Q 8
♡ —
♢ A Q J 9 6 4 3 2
♣ 7 2

The slam is certain. South should win the trump lead in dummy, ruff a heart, lead a club to dummy's ace, ruff another heart, and lead a club to the king.

Next, South should lead a spade from dummy and beat East's card as cheaply as possible. Assuming West wins this trick, he is end-played: a spade lead will be into declarer's major tenace; a heart lead will give declarer a ruff-sluff; and if West has a club to lead, a lead of that suit will establish a discard in dummy. The key to the end play is for declarer to cash both of dummy's high clubs before starting spades—if he does not do this, a club exit by West will leave declarer with a guess.

PROBLEM 53

Rubber bridge
North-South vulnerable

NORTH
♠ 9 5 2
♡ 8 4
◇ K 10 8
♣ A K J 9 6

SOUTH
♠ A Q 7
♡ —
◇ A Q J 9 6 4 3 2
♣ 8 2

SOUTH	WEST	NORTH	EAST
2 ◇	Pass	3 ♣	Pass
3 ◇	Pass	6 ◇	(All pass)

West leads a trump; East follows.

What is the best play for the contract? Is the slam certain?

SOLUTION 53

```
              ♠ 9 5 2
              ♡ 8 4
              ◇ K 10 8
              ♣ A K J 9 6

♠ K J 6 3                        ♠ 10 8 4
♡ Q 9 7 6 5 3 2                  ♡ A K J 10
◇ 7                              ◇ 5
♣ 5                              ♣ Q 10 7 4 3

              ♠ A Q 7
              ♡ —
              ◇ A Q J 9 6 4 3 2
              ♣ 8 2
```

This slam is certain. With the spade eight demoted to a seven, the end-play in spades may not succeed: East can use his intermediate spades to prevent South from ducking the lead to West.

However, the corresponding promotion of the club seven to the eight gives South a sure thing with a different line of play. He should win the opening lead, cash the club ace, reenter his hand with a heart ruff, and lead the club eight. If West shows out (as in the diagram), the club eight can be ducked to East. Later, declarer uses his two trump entries to dummy to take a ruffing finesse against East's club queen, and chases two club winners for spade discards.

If West follows to the club eight, declarer finesses the club jack. If East wins, one club ruff will establish the suit for two discards.

PROBLEM 54

Rubber bridge
Neither side vulnerable

NORTH
♠ K 4 3 2
♡ K J 4 3
♢ Q 5 2
♣ 8 6

SOUTH
♠ A Q J 10 8 5
♡ A 5 2
♢ A 10 3
♣ 2

SOUTH	WEST	NORTH	EAST
1 ♠	Pass	2 ♠	Pass
4 ♠	(All pass)		

West leads the spade nine.

Plan the play. Is the contract assured?

```
                  ♠ K 4 3 2
                  ♡ K J 4 3
                  ♢ Q 5 2
                  ♣ 8 6

♠ 9                                 ♠ 7 6
♡ 8 6                               ♡ Q 10 9 7
♢ J 9 8 7                           ♢ K 6 4
♣ K J 9 5 4 3                       ♣ A Q 10 7

                  ♠ A Q J 10 8 5
                  ♡ A 5 2
                  ♢ A 10 3
                  ♣ 2
```

Yes, the contract is assured. Declarer draws trumps, cashes the two top hearts, and leads a club. The defense must lead a second club (a diamond lead will resolve declarer's problem in that suit, and a heart lead from either side will establish a heart trick in dummy for a discard); declarer *discards his remaining heart.*

This sets the defense a problem it cannot resolve. A diamond lead will still solve that suit, and a heart lead from West will establish a discard. The only chance for the defense, therefore, is for East to win the second club and lead a heart—but declarer counters this by discarding a diamond.

It (almost) goes without saying that declarer should draw trumps without disturbing dummy's spade king, which may be needed for a late reentry in some variations.

PROBLEM 55

Rubber bridge
Neither side vulnerable

        NORTH
        ♠ K 4 3 2
        ♡ K J 4 3
        ◇ J 5 2
        ♣ Q J

        SOUTH
        ♠ A Q J 10 8 5
        ♡ A 5 2
        ◇ A 10 3
        ♣ 2

SOUTH	WEST	NORTH	EAST
1 ♠	Pass	2 ♠	Pass
4 ♠	(All pass)		

West leads the spade nine.

Plan the play. Is the contract assured?

♠ K 4 3 2
♡ K J 4 3
◇ J 5 2
♣ Q J

♠ 9 6
♡ Q 10 9 7
◇ K Q 9
♣ 9 7 5 4 3

♠ 7
♡ 8 6
◇ 8 7 6 4
♣ A K 10 8 6

♠ A Q J 10 8 5
♡ A 5 2
◇ A 10 3
♣ 2

This contract is not assured. However, it takes a minor miracle to defeat it. Declarer starts as in Solution 54, drawing three rounds of trumps without using dummy's king, cashes the heart ace-king and leads a club. For the defense to have any chance at all, East must win and lead a diamond. Declarer ducks, and West must win and play another club to East's remaining honor.

This time, however, instead of discarding on the second club, declarer should ruff and go after a heart trick on his own. If this fails (because East holds four hearts to the queen), declarer later falls back on a diamond finesse.

For the contract to be defeated, East must hold the club ace-king and four hearts to the queen; West must hold the diamond king-queen.

PROBLEM 56

IMP scoring
Both sides vulnerable

NORTH
♠ K 6 4 3
♡ J
◇ 5 4 3 2
♣ A 10 5 2

SOUTH
♠ A 8
♡ 5
◇ A K Q J 10 9
♣ K 6 4 3

SOUTH	WEST	NORTH	EAST
1 ◇	Pass	1 ♠	Pass
3 ◇	Pass	5 ◇	(All pass)

(1) West leads the eight of diamonds. *Plan the play.*

(2) West leads the heart king and shifts to the eight of diamonds.

Plan the play.

♠ K 6 4 3
♡ J
◇ 5 4 3 2
♣ A 10 5 2

♠ J 9 7 5   ♠ Q 10 4
♡ K Q 9 7 4 2   ♡ A 10 8 6 3
◇ 8 7   ◇ 6
♣ 7   ♣ Q J 9 8

♠ A 8
♡ 5
◇ A K Q J 10 9
♣ K 6 4 3

(1) There is no problem against a trump lead: Draw the trumps; then two high spades and a spade ruff, club ace, spade ruff, exit with a heart. Whoever wins this trick is end-played, and declarer loses only one club trick even if the suit is distributed 4-1. (If a club honor is led, declarer ducks.)

(2) If the defense cashes its heart first, the contract is not assured, although there is a plan with a high probability of success. Win the trump shift, draw trumps; then two spades and a spade ruff, king and another club. If West follows to this trick, declarer covers his card and loses one club trick. If West shows out on the second club, declarer wins dummy's ace and leads the last spade, discarding a club from his hand. This leads to an end-play if West has the defenders' spade length.

PROBLEM 57

Rubber bridge
Neither side vulnerable

NORTH
♠ A 4 3
♡ Q 9 6
◇ A Q 8
♣ 10 8 6 2

SOUTH
♠ 10 6 2
♡ K 10
◇ K J 4
♣ A K Q 5 3

SOUTH	WEST	NORTH	EAST
1 NT	Pass	3 NT	(All pass)

West leads the spade seven. *When should South take the spade ace? What should he do after taking it?*

♠ A 4 3
♡ Q 9 6
♢ A Q 8
♣ 10 8 6 2

♠ K J 9 7   ♠ Q 8 5
♡ 8 7 3 2   ♡ A J 5 4
♢ 7 6 5 3 2   ♢ 10 9
♣ —   ♣ J 9 7 4

♠ 10 6 2
♡ K 10
♢ K J 4
♣ A K Q 5 3

South should take the spade ace on the third round of the suit. If the suit could be blocked by taking the ace on the first trick, two ducks will do as well, except when East holds king-queen-jack tripleton and West led the seven from 9-8-7-5. It is more likely that the double hold-up will be necessary in case spades are four-three and the opponent with the tripleton spade gains the lead.

After taking the spade ace, declarer should lead the *ten* of clubs from dummy. This gives him his best chance to pick up the club suit because it tempts East to cover if he holds J-9-7-4. If declarer must lose a club trick and he judges the clubs and long spade are together, he should finesse the other opponent for the jack of hearts, but if he judges that (say) West holds the long spade and East shows up with the clubs, he should lead a heart to his king, and play on clubs if this holds. If West holds up his heart ace, more power to him.

PROBLEM 58

Rubber bridge
East-West vulnerable

NORTH
♠ K 10 8 7
♡ A 5 4 3
♢ A J 6 5 3
♣ —

SOUTH
♠ A Q J 9 6
♡ K 2
♢ 2
♣ 9 8 6 5 4

SOUTH	WEST	NORTH	EAST
1 ♠	Pass	4 ♣	Pass
6 ♠	Pass	7 ♠	(All pass)

West leads the spade deuce. East follows.

Plan the play.

SOLUTION 58

```
              ♠ K 10 8 7
              ♡ A 5 4 3
              ◇ A J 6 5 3
              ♣ —

  ♠ 2                      ♠ 5 4 3
  ♡ J 9 8 7 6              ♡ Q 10
  ◇ 10 9 8 7 4            ◇ K Q
  ♣ A Q                    ♣ K J 10 7 3 2

              ♠ A Q J 9 6
              ♡ K 2
              ◇ 2
              ♣ 9 8 6 5 4
```

This isn't a very good contract, but South should still try
to make the most of his chances. Even if all the trumps
remaining are made separately there are only 11 winners,
so the main chance is finding the king-queen of diamonds
tripleton, thus setting up two additional diamond tricks in
dummy. This requires three club ruffs in dummy as well,
so the heart ace must be the entry to the diamonds.

Thus, the correct line is: spade nine, club ruff, heart
king, club ruff, diamond ace, diamond ruff, draw trumps.
If the diamond honors have dropped and the suit was 4-3,
dummy is now high. And there is an additional chance: if,
as in the diagram, East has king-queen doubleton of
diamonds and at most two hearts, West will be squeezed
positionally on the lead of South's last trump.

PROBLEM 59

Rubber bridge
Both sides vulnerable

        NORTH
        ♠ K Q
        ♡ A J 7 3 2
        ♢ 5 2
        ♣ A 10 3 2

        SOUTH
        ♠ A J 2
        ♡ Q 8 4
        ♢ A 8 3
        ♣ K Q J 6

SOUTH	WEST	NORTH	EAST
1 NT	Pass	3 ♡	Pass
4 ♣	Pass	6 ♣	(All pass)

West leads the spade ten. Both defenders follow to the king and queen of clubs. *How should South play? Is the contract certain?*

♠ K Q
♡ A J 7 3 2
◊ 5 2
♣ A 10 3 2

♠ 10 9 8 7 4 3   ♠ 6 5
♡ —   ♡ K 10 9 6 5
◊ K 10 9 7   ◊ Q J 6 4
♣ 9 5 4   ♣ 8 7

♠ A J 2
♡ Q 8 4
◊ A 8 3
♣ K Q J 6

Declarer should draw a third round of trumps in dummy and lead a heart to his queen. Unless West shows out there is no problem (if hearts are not 5-0 one ruff at worst will establish them; if West has five hearts, declarer can finesse against the 10-9). If West does show out, declarer runs two more spade tricks, throwing a diamond from dummy. East must keep all his hearts (else a duck, then a later heart ruff, will establish an extra heart trick). Then, ace of diamonds and a diamond ruff and a low heart will end-play East.

The contract is not quite assured. This play will fail if East, in addition to his five hearts and two (or three) clubs, has four or more spades.

PROBLEM 60

Matchpoints
East-West vulnerable

NORTH
♠ K 5 4 3
♡ K 8
♢ K Q
♣ A 6 4 3 2

SOUTH
♠ A Q 10 6 2
♡ 5 4 3 2
♢ A J 6
♣ 9

SOUTH	WEST	NORTH	EAST
1 ♠	Pass	3 ♣	Pass
3 ♠	Pass	4 ♠	(All pass)

West leads the heart ace, East playing the queen. East trumps the next heart and leads a diamond to dummy's king. On a spade lead to the ace, West plays a heart.

What is the best play for an overtrick?

SOLUTION 60

♠ K 5 4 3
♡ K 8
♢ K Q
♣ A 6 4 3 2

♠ —
♡ A J 10 9 7 6
♢ 10 8 7
♣ Q 10 8 5

♠ J 9 8 7
♡ Q
♢ 9 5 4 3 2
♣ K J 7

♠ A Q 10 6 2
♡ 5 4 3 2
♢ A J 6
♣ 9

The contract is easy, but an overtrick may be necessary for a good matchpoint score. The best chance is to play West for four or more clubs. In that case he can be squeezed in hearts and clubs. Declarer should lead a club to dummy's ace and a spade to his own ten, a diamond to the queen, ruff a club, cash the ace of diamonds, and lead the spade *queen*. If West, on this trick, comes down to a singleton heart, declarer lets the spade queen hold, ruffs a heart, and takes the rest in his hand.

If West keeps two hearts, declarer overtakes the spade queen, ruffs a club, and takes the rest in dummy.

We could have made your job more difficult by not telling you to lead the first spade to the ace (rather than the *queen*), but perhaps it's hard enough as it is.

PROBLEM 61

Rubber bridge
Both sides vulnerable

> **NORTH**
> ♠ A Q
> ♡ 9 6 2
> ◇ 5 3
> ♣ A K 9 8 6 3
>
> **SOUTH**
> ♠ J 5 2
> ♡ A K J 10 8 4
> ◇ Q
> ♣ 5 4 2

SOUTH	WEST	NORTH	EAST
—	—	1 ♣	Pass
1 ♡	Pass	2 ♡	Pass
4 ♡	(All pass)		

West leads the spade six: queen, king. East leads a diamond to West's ace, and West returns a diamond.

Plan the play.

♠ A Q
♡ 9 6 2
◇ 5 3
♣ A K 9 8 6 3

♠ 10 8 7 6 4   ♠ K 9 3
♡ Q 7   ♡ 5 3
◇ A J 10 7 2   ◇ K 9 8 6 4
♣ J   ♣ Q 10 7

♠ J 5 2
♡ A K J 10 8 4
◇ Q
♣ 5 4 2

After ruffing the second diamond, South should play spade ace, heart ace, spade jack, club ace, and lead a trump from dummy. Assuming East follows small to the second trump, declarer should then finesse.

This is slightly the inferior method of handling the trump suit, but it assures the contract (assuming no early defensive ruff) when West has a singleton club. If South tries to drop the heart queen and is wrong, he will need a 2-2 club split; but if he finesses and is wrong, he goes down only if West holds the long clubs.

PROBLEM 62

Matchpoints

Both sides vulnerable

> NORTH
> ♠ K 5 2
> ♡ K 4
> ◇ 8 6 4 2
> ♣ 10 5 4 3
>
> SOUTH
> ♠ A J 7 6 4 3
> ♡ A 8 2
> ◇ A K 5
> ♣ A

SOUTH	WEST	NORTH	EAST
1 ♠	Pass	2 ♠	Pass
3 ♡	Pass	4 ♠	Pass
6 ♠	(All pass)		

West leads the heart queen. *How should declarer play? What is the percentage play in trumps?*

SOLUTION 62

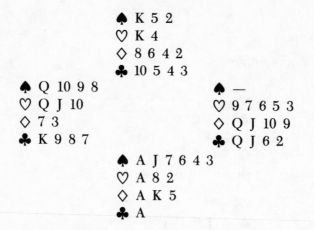

♠ K 5 2
♡ K 4
◇ 8 6 4 2
♣ 10 5 4 3

♠ Q 10 9 8
♡ Q J 10
◇ 7 3
♣ K 9 8 7

♠ —
♡ 9 7 6 5 3
◇ Q J 10 9
♣ Q J 6 2

♠ A J 7 6 4 3
♡ A 8 2
◇ A K 5
♣ A

Considering just the spade suit, the percentage play (by a narrow margin) is to cash the king and ace. However, one West leads the heart queen, and can therefore be presumed to hold the heart jack (and very likely the ten and/or nine as well), the percentage play in spades (by a very narrow margin) is to cash the king and finesse East for the spade queen.

All this, however, has nothing to do with how to play this hand. Regardless of how declarer intends to play against a normal break, he should take precautions against a 4-0 split by winning the first trick in his hand with the heart ace and cashing the ace of clubs.

Now a spade to the king and, if spades are not 4-0, declarer must guess the spades to bring in the contract. But if spades are 4-0, declarer can try for an end-play as follows: club ruff (*not* a spade finesse, even if West showed out), diamond ace-king, heart king, club ruff, heart ruff, club ruff, diamond. If all has gone well, an opponent will be down to three trumps for his last three cards, and South will score the spade ace-jack at the end. Note the importance of preserving the heart-king entry to dummy.

PROBLEM 63

Matchpoints
East-West vulnerable

> NORTH
> ♠ A K Q 6 4 2
> ♡ K 6
> ♢ 4 3 2
> ♣ A 2
>
> SOUTH
> ♠ 5
> ♡ A Q J 10 9 8 7
> ♢ A 6 5
> ♣ 6 4

SOUTH	WEST	NORTH	EAST
—	—	1 ♠	Pass
3 ♡	Pass	3 ♠	Pass
4 ♡	Pass	5 ♣	Pass
5 ♢	Pass	7 ♡	(All pass)

West leads the club queen.

Plan the play.

SOLUTION 63

♠ A K Q 6 4 2
♡ K 6
◇ 4 3 2
♣ A 2

♠ J 9 8 7   ♠ 10 3
♡ 3 2   ♡ 5 4
◇ K 8 7   ◇ Q J 10 9
♣ Q J 10 8   ♣ K 9 7 5 3

♠ 5
♡ A Q J 10 9 8 7
◇ A 6 5
♣ 6 4

After winning the ace of clubs, declarer should lead the heart six from dummy. If trumps break 4-0, declarer has no choice but to draw trumps, run the rest of his trumps, and hope for the best.

Assuming trumps do not break 4-0, South faces a close percentage question. With a 4-0 trump break eliminated, the chance of a 2-2 trump split is 45%. (The chances of 3-1 and 2-2 trump splits, originally roughly 49.7% and 40.7% respectively, maintain the same ratio but now must add to 100%, thus becoming 55% and 45% respectively.) So, by playing ace and a low spade, ruffing in his hand, then leading a heart to dummy, declarer makes whenever spades are 3-3 or 4-2 (about 84%) and trumps are 2-2 (about 45%); almost 38% of the time.

The alternative play, running all the trumps, makes the contract whenever spades are 3-3 (about 36%), or if the opponents make a mistake in the ending. Against strong opposition, therefore, playing for trumps to be 2-2 is probably the best play. In any event, the two lines of play are virtually equivalent in merit.

PROBLEM 64

Matchpoints
East-West vulnerable

> NORTH
> ♠ A K Q 6 4 2
> ♡ K 6
> ◇ J 4 2
> ♣ A 6
>
> SOUTH
> ♠ 5
> ♡ A Q J 10 9 8 7
> ◇ A 10 4
> ♣ 9 4

SOUTH	WEST	NORTH	EAST
—	—	1 ♠	Pass
3 ♡	Pass	3 ♠	Pass
4 ♡	Pass	5 ♣	Pass
5 ◇	Pass	7 ♡	(All pass)

West leads the club queen.

Plan the play.

SOLUTION 64

    ♣ A K Q 6 4 2
    ♡ K 6
    ◇ J 4 2
    ♣ A 6

♠ 10 3   ♠ J 9 8 7
♡ 2   ♡ 5 4 3
◇ 8 7 6 3   ◇ K Q 9
♣ Q J 10 8 3 2   ♣ K 7 5

    ♠ 5
    ♡ A Q J 10 9 8 7
    ◇ A 10 4
    ♣ 9 4

In contrast to the previous problem, here it is much better to run off the heart suit (being careful to discard the *jack* of diamonds from dummy on the last heart).

There is a chance for a simple squeeze if, as here, the opponent who guards spades also holds the king-queen of diamonds. (And, for you squeeze experts, if West holds the spades and one diamond honor there is a double guard squeeze. It is true that declarer may misguess the diamond position in the ending, but the club nine in the closed hand limits the false-carding opportunities of the defense; the declarer should guess right most of the time even against expert opponents.)

PROBLEM 65

Rubber bridge
Both sides vulnerable

NORTH
♠ K 7 5 3 2
♡ A Q 5 3 2
◇ K 6
♣ 5

SOUTH
♠ 10 6 4
♡ K J 10 9 7 6
◇ A 8
♣ A 9

SOUTH	WEST	NORTH	EAST
1 ♡	Pass	1 ♠	Pass
2 ♠	Pass	4 NT	Pass
5 ♡	Pass	6 ♡	(All pass)

West leads the queen of diamonds.

(a) What chances do you have for the contract?
(b) How do you play against expert defenders?
(c) How do you play against weak defenders?

SOLUTION 65

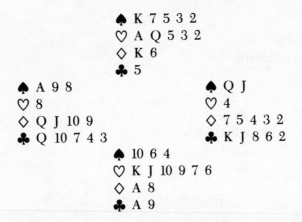

♠ K 7 5 3 2
♡ A Q 5 3 2
◇ K 6
♣ 5

♠ A 9 8   ♠ Q J
♡ 8   ♡ 4
◇ Q J 10 9   ◇ 7 5 4 3 2
♣ Q 10 7 4 3   ♣ K J 8 6 2

♠ 10 6 4
♡ K J 10 9 7 6
◇ A 8
♣ A 9

Things don't look too good. Against perfect defense, the only chances are (1) singleton ace of spades with West; (2) singleton ace of spades (and no chances to discard it) with East; (3) queen-jack doubleton of spades (and no chance to discard one) with East. The best you can do against perfect defense is combine (1) and (3): draw trumps, eliminate the minors, and lead a spade to the king.

Against weak defenders there are some further chances. For example if West has the spade ace *doubleton* he may duck it. In order to induce this, declarer might want to lead the spade *ten* from his hand, either before or after the elimination. The value of leading the ten is that it may appear to West as if South is about to take a finesse against the queen. Perhaps, therefore, the best time to try this deception is *after drawing trumps*, but before eliminating the minors. (It would be unnatural for declarer to start spades before drawing trumps, and this may alert the West player.) This play gives up chances (1) and (3).

A compromise is to lead the spade ten after the elimination. This gives up chance (3), but not chance (1). A poor defender may fail to count the hand, and play South for four spades.

PROBLEM 66

Rubber bridge
North-South vulnerable

> NORTH
> ♠ 9 8 5
> ♡ A 10 9 8 4
> ♢ 6 3 2
> ♣ 8 4
>
> SOUTH
> ♠ A K Q J 3 2
> ♡ K Q 3
> ♢ A Q
> ♣ A Q

SOUTH	WEST	NORTH	EAST
2 ♠	Pass	3 ♡	Pass
3 ♠	Pass	4 ♠	Pass
6 NT	(All pass)		

West leads the spade seven.

Plan the play.

SOLUTION 66

♠ 9 8 5
♡ A 10 9 8 4
◇ 6 3 2
♣ 8 4

♠ 10 7 4
♡ 2
◇ K 10 8 7
♣ K 10 7 6 3

♠ 6
♡ J 7 6 5
◇ J 9 5 4
♣ J 9 5 4

♠ A K Q J 3 2
♡ K Q 3
◇ A Q
♣ A Q

Declarer should duck the first lead in dummy, win in the closed hand, cash the heart king, and (if both opponents follow) lead the heart three to dummy's eight. If this is captured by East, South has 12 top tricks.

If the heart eight holds, declarer can cash the heart queen, force entry to dummy by successively leading his low spades, and get five spades, five hearts and two aces.

If West shows out on the first heart, declarer can force heart entries to dummy for two minor-suit finesses.

PROBLEM 67

IMP scoring;
East-West vulnerable

> **NORTH**
> ♠ K J 9 3
> ♡ 8 6 3
> ◇ K Q 10 2
> ♣ 8 6
>
> **SOUTH**
> ♠ A 10 8 6 4 2
> ♡ A K 9
> ◇ 5 4 3
> ♣ A

SOUTH	WEST	NORTH	EAST
1 ♠	Pass	3 ♠	Pass
4 ♠	(All pass)		

West leads the club queen.

Plan the play.

    ♠ K J 9 3
    ♡ 8 6 3
    ◇ K Q 10 2
    ♣ 8 6

♠ —   ♠ Q 7 5
♡ Q 10 5 4 2   ♡ J 7
◇ 8 6   ◇ A J 9 7
♣ Q J 10 5 4 3 ♣ K 9 7 2

    ♠ A 10 8 6 4 2
    ♡ A K 9
    ◇ 5 4 3
    ♣ A

After winning the club ace, South should cash the ace of spades. Unless West shows out, there is no further problem.

If West is void of spades, declarer enters dummy with the spade king and ruffs dummy's last club. Now he leads ace, king and nine of hearts. If East wins he can cash the spade queen, but then must lead diamonds into dummy's tenace.

If West wins the heart queen and leads a diamond, declarer goes up with dummy's king. If East wins he is end-played. If the diamond king wins, a trump lead from the dummy end-plays East.

Note that the contract is certain to be fulfilled with this line of play, whereas if South leads a spade to the king and *East* is void, defeat is possible.

PROBLEM 68

IMP scoring
East-West vulnerable

> NORTH
> ♠ K 9 7 3
> ♡ 8 6 3
> ◇ K Q 10 2
> ♣ 8 6
>
> SOUTH
> ♠ A 8 6 5 4 2
> ♡ A K 4
> ◇ 9 4 3
> ♣ A

SOUTH	WEST	NORTH	EAST
1 ♠	Pass	3 ♠	Pass
4 ♠	(All pass)		

West leads the club queen.

Plan the play.

SOLUTION 68

♠ K 9 7 3
♡ 8 6 3
◇ K Q 10 2
♣ 8 6

♠ Q J 10   ♠ —
♡ Q 10 5 2   ♡ J 9 7
◇ 8 6   ◇ A J 7 5
♣ Q J 10 5   ♣ K 9 7 4 3 2

♠ A 8 6 5 4 2
♡ A K 4
◇ 9 4 3
♣ A

Cash the spade ace after winning the club ace. If both opponents follow, the contract is assured.

If East is void of spades, South should begin diamonds at once, leading towards dummy's king. If the diamond king loses to the ace and a heart is returned (best), South wins and leads a diamond to dummy's queen and plays another diamond, establishing a discard in dummy with the spade king for entry.

If the diamond king holds, declarer can continue diamonds to set up a discard—and he might as well do it by ruffing a club and leading once again toward dummy's holding.

PROBLEM 69

Rubber bridge
Neither side vulnerable

NORTH
♠ 6 2
♡ 5 4 3
◇ A Q 8
♣ A Q 6 4 2

SOUTH
♠ A K
♡ K 7 6 2
◇ K J 10 9 6
♣ K 3

SOUTH	WEST	NORTH	EAST
1 ◇	Pass	2 ♣	Pass
3 NT	Pass	4 ◇	Pass
4 ♠	Pass	5 ♣	Pass
6 ◇	(All pass)		

West leads a trump and both opponents follow to the ace and jack.

Plan the play.

```
                    ♠ 6 2
                    ♡ 5 4 3
                    ◇ A Q 8
                    ♣ A Q 6 4 2
♠ Q 10 9 3                          ♠ J 8 7 5 4
♡ Q 10                             ♡ A J 9 8
◇ 7 5 4                            ◇ 3 2
♣ 10 8 7 5                         ♣ J 9
                    ♠ A K
                    ♡ K 7 6 2
                    ◇ K J 10 9 6
                    ♣ K 3
```

Plan One: Draw the last trump and try to run the clubs. This requires a 3-3 club split—about a 36% chance.

Plan Two: Before drawing the third trump, play king, ace and ruff a club. Then play a trump to dummy, cash the long club, and play East for the heart ace. For success, this play requires no worse than a 4-2 club split (about 84%) and the heart ace with East—a total chance of roughly 42%.

Plan Three: Before drawing the third trump, play king, ace and queen of clubs. If clubs are 3-3, draw the last trump from dummy. If clubs are 4-2 and the queen is not ruffed, ruff a club, reenter dummy with a trump, cash the long club, and play East for the heart ace. Plan Three lands the contract if clubs are 3-3 (36%) and if clubs are 4-2 (48%) provided East has the heart ace and the long trump is with the long clubs. The chance of the long trump and long clubs being together is somewhat *less* than 50%, so declarer wins out slightly less than 25% of the times that the clubs break 4-2 (actually, about 22.5% of the time). Nonetheless, the additional 11% that declarer gains from the 4-2 club splits (.225 times .48) makes Plan Three the best.

PROBLEM 70

Rubber bridge
East-West vulnerable

            NORTH
            ♠ K 6
            ♡ A 8 4
            ◇ 10 9 8 7 3 2
            ♣ A 8

            SOUTH
            ♠ Q 7 5 3 2
            ♡ K Q 6
            ◇ A Q
            ♣ K 6 4

SOUTH	WEST	NORTH	EAST
1 ♠	Pass	2 ◇	Pass
2 NT	Pass	3 NT	(All pass)

West leads the club deuce. Assuming clubs are 4-4, *how should South play?*

SOLUTION 70

```
                    ♠ K 6
                    ♡ A 8 4
                    ◇ 10 9 8 7 3 2
                    ♣ A 8
    ♠ A J 9 4                        ♠ 10 8
    ♡ 10 2                           ♡ J 9 7 5 3
    ◇ J 6 5                          ◇ K 4
    ♣ Q 10 3 2                       ♣ J 9 7 5
                    ♠ Q 7 5 3 2
                    ♡ K Q 6
                    ◇ A Q
                    ♣ K 6 4
```

Declarer has a choice of two direct and one indirect line of play. The two direct lines are: (1) Win the club ace, finesse the queen of diamonds; (2) Win the club king, play ace and queen of diamonds. Between these, play (1) gives up a necessary entry to dummy. Plan (2), which succeeds if there is a singleton diamond honor or a doubleton jack, has roughly a one-third chance of success.

The indirect play is superior to both. Declarer should win the club king in the closed hand and lead a spade. Then:

(i) If West plays the spade ace, the contract can be brought home if spades are 3-3 or 4-2, or if the diamond finesse wins.

(ii) If East tops the spade king with the ace, declarer will need a 3-3 spade split.

(iii) If the spade king wins, declarer can take the diamond finesse. If this loses, declarer retains the chance of a doubleton diamond jack. If the diamond finesse wins, declarer can try to set up diamonds, and has chances even if this proves impossible.

The indirect play is never worse than 36% (actually it's about 50% and is thus superior to either of the direct plans).

PROBLEM 71

Rubber bridge
Both sides vulnerable

> **NORTH**
> ♠ J 10 8 5 3
> ♡ A 8 6 4 2
> ◇ K Q 2
> ♣ —
>
> **SOUTH**
> ♠ A K Q 9
> ♡ K 5
> ◇ 6 4 3
> ♣ K J 10 6

SOUTH	WEST	NORTH	EAST
1 NT	Pass	2 ♣	Pass
2 ♠	Pass	6 ♠	(All pass)

West leads the diamond jack, king, *ace*, three. East returns the diamond five.

Plan the play.

SOLUTION 71

♠ J 10 8 5 3	
♡ A 8 6 4 2	
◇ K Q 2	
♣ —	

♠ 7 6 2	♠ 4
♡ 10 9	♡ Q J 7 3
◇ J 10 9	◇ A 8 7 5
♣ A Q 9 8 2	♣ 7 5 4 3

♠ A K Q 9
♡ K 5
◇ 6 4 3
♣ K J 10 6

Unless spades are 2-2 and hearts 3-3, declarer will need to establish a club trick (through a double ruffing finesse, West holding both ace and queen) for his contract. In order to give himself the best chance of setting up this trick, he should begin by playing king, ace and a third heart, ruffing high. If hearts break 4-2, declarer starts clubs at once, leading the king and letting it ride if not covered.

If hearts break 3-3, declarer plays one round of trumps. If trumps are 4-0, he begins clubs. If not, he leads the club king from his hand, tempting West to cover. If West ducks, declarer should ruff in dummy—hoping for a 2-2 trump split, which is more likely than finding West with both club honors. However, by leading the club king, South has a chance to play on clubs if spades are not 2-2: West may err in covering the club king. Note that it would do no good for South to draw a second trump, as he would then lack the entries to set up a club trick.

PROBLEM 72

Rubber bridge
Neither side vulnerable

> NORTH
> ♠ 10 9 4 2
> ♡ 6
> ◇ 9 3 2
> ♣ K Q 7 4 3
>
> SOUTH
> ♠ K J
> ♡ A 8 5 2
> ◇ A K Q J 10
> ♣ 6 2

SOUTH	WEST	NORTH	EAST
—	Pass	Pass	Pass
1 ◇	Pass	1 ♠	Pass
2 ♡	Pass	3 ◇	Pass
Pass	Pass		

West leads the diamond five. East plays the eight.

Plan the play.

SOLUTION 72

```
              ♠ 10 9 4 2
              ♡ 6
              ◇ 9 3 2
              ♣ K Q 7 4 3
♠ A Q 5                      ♠ 8 7 6 3
♡ K J 4                      ♡ Q 10 9 7 3
◇ 7 5 4                      ◇ 8 6
♣ J 10 9 5                   ♣ A 8
              ♠ K J
              ♡ A 8 5 2
              ◇ A K Q J 10
              ♣ 6 2
```

South has several lines of play open to him. He could ruff a heart in dummy immediately but the opponents will almost surely lead another trump before South can return to his hand for a second heart ruff. Alternatively, South could attempt to establish dummy's club suit. This, however, depends on a very favorable lie of the enemy clubs—and even if South is lucky he will not be sure how to proceed if the first club holds in dummy.

In either of the above attempts, South may be forced to depend on making a quick spade trick, and may be defeated if he misguesses spades or if West has both honors. If instead, however, South sets out *immediately* to establish a spade trick—by leading the spade king from his hand at the second trick—only a highly adverse distribution of the unseen cards can defeat him.

If, for example, East-West win and lead another trump, declarer can knock out the remaining spade honor, with both a trump in dummy and the heart ace available to stop the heart suit.

PROBLEM 73

Rubber bridge
Neither side vulnerable

NORTH
♠ Q 4 3 2
♡ 8 6 4
◇ K Q
♣ K J 9 8

SOUTH
♠ K 10 6 5
♡ A J
◇ J 6 2
♣ A Q 10 2

SOUTH	WEST	NORTH	EAST
—	Pass	Pass	Pass
1 NT	Pass	2 ♣	Pass
2 ♠	Pass	4 ♠	Pass
Pass	Pass		

West leads the heart king. East plays the deuce.

Plan the play.

♠ Q 4 3 2
♡ 8 6 4
◇ K Q
♣ K J 9 8

♠ J 9 7   ♠ A 8
♡ K Q 10 9   ♡ 7 5 3 2
◇ A 8 7 4   ◇ 10 9 5 3
♣ 6 4   ♣ 7 5 3

♠ K 10 6 5
♡ A J
◇ J 6 2
♣ A Q 10 2

After winning the first trick, declarer should drive out the ace of diamonds. This is not because he is in a great hurry to establish diamonds—rather, he wants to discover who holds the diamond ace before leading trumps.

If East shows up with the diamond ace, declarer should take the normal play in trumps—leading to the queen and then to the ten. But if West holds the diamond ace—marking East with the trump ace (because of West's failure to open the bidding)—declarer should play trumps by leading first to the *king* and, if that holds, ducking the next round (unless West plays the jack).

South must assume trumps are 3-2. If East is known to hold the ace, playing to the queen and ten will win if East holds A-J, A-J-9, A-J-8, A-J-7 (four cases). But leading to the king first will win when East has A-J, A-9, A-8, A-7, A-9-8, A-9-7, A-8-7 (seven cases).

PROBLEM 74

Rubber bridge
Neither side vulnerable

> NORTH
> ♠ A Q 8 6
> ♡ A Q J
> ◇ 5 4 3
> ♣ K J 4
>
> SOUTH
> ♠ K J 10 9 2
> ♡ 4
> ◇ K 9 7 2
> ♣ A 10 3

SOUTH	WEST	NORTH	EAST
—	—	1 NT	Pass
3 ♠	Pass	4 ♠	(All pass)

West leads the spade five. East plays the three.

Plan the play.

SOLUTION 74

```
              ♠ A Q 8 6
              ♡ A Q J
              ◇ 5 4 3
              ♣ K J 4
♠ 5                        ♠ 7 4 3
♡ K 8 6 5 3                ♡ 10 9 7 2
◇ A Q 10 8                 ◇ J 6
♣ 8 7 5                    ♣ Q 9 6 2
              ♠ K J 10 9 2
              ♡ 4
              ◇ K 9 7 2
              ♣ A 10 3
```

Plan One. Win the trump, heart ace, heart ruff, spade to dummy, heart ruff. Now if trumps were 2-2, lead a low diamond and duck a second round of diamonds by the defense; the contract is assured. If trumps were 3-1, draw the third trump and take finesses in diamonds and clubs.

Plan Two. Win the trump, draw trumps, cash the ace of hearts, and lead a diamond from dummy, covering East's card. Even if trumps were 3-1, this play will lead to a successful end-play of West (or the straight establishment of a diamond trick for a club discard from dummy) unless East began with the doubleton Q-J, Q-10 or J-10 of diamonds. And even in this instance, declarer can still recover with a successful club finesse.

Even though you would choose Plan One if you knew the trumps were splitting 2-2, Plan Two is the best overall approach. The probability of finding East with a "killing" diamond holding is very low (less than 5%), and there is still the club finesse in reserve. Two losing finesses with a 3-1 trump break is a greater risk.

PROBLEM 75

Rubber bridge
East-West vulnerable

> **NORTH**
> ♠ A 10 5
> ♡ A Q
> ◇ 5 4 3 2
> ♣ 6 5 4 2
>
> **SOUTH**
> ♠ K J 2
> ♡ J 6 2
> ◇ A Q
> ♣ A K Q 8 3

SOUTH	WEST	NORTH	EAST
1 ♣	Pass	1 ◇	Pass
2 NT	Pass	3 NT	(All pass)

West leads the heart five.

Plan the play.

SOLUTION 75

```
            ♠ A 10 5
            ♡ A Q
            ◇ 5 4 3 2
            ♣ 6 5 4 2

♠ 7 6 4 3                    ♠ Q 9 8
♡ 10 8 7 5 4                 ♡ K 9 3
◇ K 9 7 6                    ◇ J 10 8
♣ —                          ♣ J 10 9 7

            ♠ K J 2
            ♡ J 6 2
            ◇ A Q
            ♣ A K Q 8 3
```

South should put up dummy's heart ace in order to avoid the dangerous diamond shift. After doing so, his only problem is to bring in the club suit, so he should lead a low club from dummy and, if East plays the seven, cover it with the eight. If this loses, declarer has time to establish a ninth trick in hearts.

If East inserts a high club and West shows out, South should lead and pass the spade jack. If this wins, the ninth trick can be set up in hearts. If the spade jack loses, declarer has two spade entries to dummy to finesse clubs and run that suit.

PROBLEM 76

Rubber bridge
Neither side vulnerable

NORTH
♠ 9 4 3 2
♡ 5 4 2
♢ A 10 9 3 2
♣ 4

SOUTH
♠ A K 10 5
♡ A K Q 6
♢ K Q J
♣ A Q

SOUTH	WEST	NORTH	EAST
—	—	Pass	4 ♣
5 NT	Pass	6 NT	Pass
Pass	Pass		

West leads the diamond eight. East discards the club five.

Is the contract assured? If so, how? If not, how good is the chance?

SOLUTION 76

♠ 9 4 3 2
♡ 5 4 2
◇ A 10 9 3 2
♣ 4

♠ Q J 8 7	♠ 6
♡ 9	♡ J 10 8 7 3
◇ 8 7 6 5 4	◇ —
♣ K 3 2	♣ J 10 9 8 7 6 5

♠ A K 10 5
♡ A K Q 6
◇ K Q J
♣ A Q

Yes, the contract is assured. South should win the first trick in his hand and play ace and another spade. Unless East shows up with a void or small singleton in spades, there is no further problem.

Assuming West has a double spade stopper, South should win the return and cash three top hearts. If East proves to have a heart stopper, declarer can cash his other high spade and run diamonds, applying a double squeeze. (West must hold a high spade, East a high heart—South discards his own last heart if East keeps his guard in that suit on the last diamond—so neither can hold two clubs; and South wins the last trick with the club queen.)

If it turns out that *West* has a heart stopper, that player must have four spades, four hearts, five diamonds, and therefore no clubs. So, after running the diamonds, declarer—surprise!—takes a finesse: one that is guaranteed to win.

PROBLEM 77

Rubber bridge
North-South vulnerable

NORTH
♠ A J 2
♡ J 2
♢ A Q 6 4
♣ K J 6 2

SOUTH
♠ Q 10 5
♡ A Q 8 3
♢ K J 3
♣ A Q 8

SOUTH	WEST	NORTH	EAST
1 NT	Pass	4 NT	Pass
6 NT	(All pass)		

West leads the diamond nine.

Plan the play.

SOLUTION 77

<pre>
                    ♠ A J 2
                    ♡ J 2
                    ◇ A Q 6 4
                    ♣ K J 6 2
    ♠ 9 6 3   ♠ K 8 7 4
    ♡ K 10 7 4   ♡ 9 6 5
    ◇ 9 8 5   ◇ 10 7 2
    ♣ 10 5 4   ♣ 9 7 3
                    ♠ Q 10 5
                    ♡ A Q 8 3
                    ◇ K J 3
                    ♣ A Q 8
</pre>

If South starts with the spade finesse and it loses, he is
reduced to a successful heart finesse for his contract. If,
however, South starts hearts first he can give himself an
extra chance.

A good line is to win the opening lead and play a low
heart towards dummy's jack. If West has the heart king
the contract is assured: if West plays the king South has
the rest; if West ducks, South can try the spade finesse for
an overtrick.

If East captures the heart jack with the king, declarer
has time to test the hearts before going after spades. This
gives him the opportunity to try to drop the doubleton or
tripleton 10-9 of hearts.

The *best* play, however, is to cash some of the minor-
suit winners (being careful, of course, to leave enough
entries to both hands) before adopting the basic line of
play given above. If the minors show skewed distribution
with, for example, West long in both suits, declarer may
change his mind and play East for the king of hearts.

PROBLEM 78

Rubber bridge
Both sides vulnerable

NORTH
♠ 2
♡ 8 6 2
♢ A 9 5
♣ K J 10 6 3 2

SOUTH
♠ A K J
♡ K 4 3
♢ 3
♣ A Q 9 8 7 4

SOUTH	WEST	NORTH	EAST
1 ♣	Pass	3 ♣	Pass
6 ♣	(All pass)		

West leads the diamond queen.

Plan the play.

♠ 2
♡ 8 6 2
◇ A 9 5
♣ K J 10 6 3 2

♠ 10 8 7 4 3   ♠ Q 9 6 5
♡ A J 9   ♡ Q 10 7 5
◇ Q J 10 2   ◇ K 8 7 6 4
♣ 5   ♣ —

♠ A K J
♡ K 4 3
◇ 3
♣ A Q 9 8 7 4

If South were to assume that his opponents were omniscient, his best play would be to win the diamond ruff a diamond, draw the trump, ruff a diamond, cash the top spades, ruff the spade jack if the spade queen has not appeared, and lead a heart to the king. This succeeds when the heart ace is onside, or offside singleton, or when the spade queen drops singleton or doubleton.

But the "extra chances" (beyond the heart ace onside) are not worth worrying about. The correct practical play is to lead a heart to the king at trick two. If West has the heart ace he may *duck*, thinking to give declarer a choice of future plays. And even if West takes his heart ace, it is far from certain that he will return a heart—in which case declarer has a chance to win the spade finesse.

PROBLEM 79

Rubber bridge
Both sides vulnerable

> NORTH
> ♠ 6 4
> ♡ K J 10 5 2
> ◇ 9 5
> ♣ A Q 9 4
>
> SOUTH
> ♠ A J 10
> ♡ A Q 8 7 6
> ◇ K 3 2
> ♣ 5 3

SOUTH	WEST	NORTH	EAST
1 ♡	1 ♠	4 ♡	(All pass)

West leads the club jack.

Plan the play.

♠ 6 4
♡ K J 10 5 2
◊ 9 5
♣ A Q 9 4

♠ K Q 9 7 2   ♠ 8 5 3
♡ 4   ♡ 9 3
◊ A Q 8 4   ◊ J 10 7 6
♣ J 10 6   ♣ K 8 7 2

♠ A J 10
♡ A Q 8 7 6
◊ K 3 2
♣ 5 3

West, who overcalled vulnerable, is likely to hold the diamond ace and spade king-queen. Because of the relatively high probability of this honor holding, South should be willing to depend on West holding the club ten rather than follow the usual route of taking finesses in the pointed suits.

Thus, the best play is to duck the opening lead completely! If the club jack holds, either because West holds the club king or East fails to overtake, declarer can draw trumps while eliminating clubs, then lead a spade to the jack to endplay West.

If East overtakes with the club king at the first trick and shifts, declarer can later finesse the club nine to try for two spade discards.

PROBLEM 80

Rubber bridge
East-West vulnerable

NORTH
- ♠ J 10 9
- ♡ J 10 9 5 3
- ◇ 8 4 2
- ♣ 5 4

SOUTH
- ♠ A K Q 8 7 6
- ♡ A K Q
- ◇ A Q 5 3
- ♣ —

SOUTH	WEST	NORTH	EAST
2 ♣	Pass	2 ◇	Pass
2 ♠	Pass	2 NT	Pass
3 ◇	Pass	3 ♠	Pass
6 ♠	(All pass)		

West leads the club king.

Plan the play.

SOLUTION 80

```
              ♠ J 10 9
              ♡ J 10 9 5 3
              ◇ 8 4 2
              ♣ 5 4
♠ 5 4 3 2                      ♠ —
♡ 4 2                          ♡ 8 7 6
◇ J 6                          ◇ K 10 9 7
♣ A K J 10 6                   ♣ Q 9 8 7 3 2
              ♠ A K Q 8 7 6
              ♡ A K Q
              ◇ A Q 5 3
              ♣ —
```

If you planned to discard a high heart on the opening lead, you had the right idea. After this play declarer can draw two trumps, cash off the two remaining high hearts, then lead a third trump to dummy to run the rest of the heart suit. (It is more risky to try this without throwing away one high heart, for then declarer would have to try *three* rounds of hearts before drawing the third trump. This would make a defensive ruff more likely, leaving declarer to depend on the diamond finesse.)

As is often the case, however, there is no need to put this plan, good though it may be, into operation at once. The correct play is to trump the first trick high, then lead a trump to dummy. If both opponents follow, South should lead dummy's remaining club and discard a high heart, continuing as described above.

The advantage of the delaying maneuver is that declarer gets to test the trumps before committing himself. If trumps are 4-0, the heart discard plan will not work. Seeing the bad split, however, declarer can shift gears: he takes the diamond finesse and tries to ruff his long diamond in dummy.

PROBLEM 81

Rubber bridge
East-West vulnerable

> NORTH
> ♠ A Q 10 6 3
> ♡ K Q
> ◇ 5 3 2
> ♣ K 3 2
>
> SOUTH
> ♠ K J 9 5 4 2
> ♡ —
> ◇ K 7 6 4
> ♣ A J 10

SOUTH	WEST	NORTH	EAST
1 ♠	Pass	3 ♠	Pass
4 ♠	(All Pass)		

West leads the spade seven; East follows.

Plan the play.

SOLUTION 81

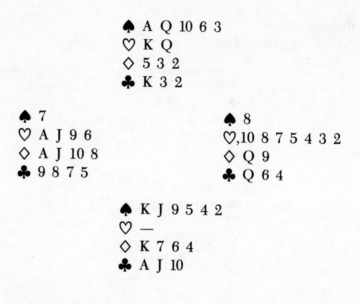

♠ A Q 10 6 3
♡ K Q
◇ 5 3 2
♣ K 3 2

♠ 7
♡ A J 9 6
◇ A J 10 8
♣ 9 8 7 5

♠ 8
♡ 10 8 7 5 4 3 2
◇ Q 9
♣ Q 6 4

♠ K J 9 5 4 2
♡ —
◇ K 7 6 4
♣ A J 10

It is easy to fall into a trap because of the largely superfluous values represented by dummy's king-queen of hearts. The contract is certain even if these are small cards.

Declarer should win the trump in dummy, ruff a heart, lead a trump to dummy, ruff the remaining heart, then exit with a small diamond. If the opponents lead a second diamond, South again plays low from both hands.

Now the defense is helpless. It must lead a diamond, setting up a trick in that suit in the closed hand, or lead a club, resolving South's problem in that suit, or concede a sluff-and-ruff.

PROBLEM 82

IMP scoring
North-South vulnerable

> NORTH
> ♠ K 4
> ♡ 8 5 3 2
> ◇ Q 8 6
> ♣ A J 7 3
>
> SOUTH
> ♠ A Q J 9 7 5
> ♡ A K Q
> ◇ A 4 3 2
> ♣ —

SOUTH	WEST	NORTH	EAST
1 ♠	Pass	2 ♣	Pass
3 ♠	Pass	4 ♠	Pass
6 ♠	Pass	Pass	Pass

West leads the club ten.

Plan the play.

```
                    ♠ K 4
                    ♡ 8 5 3 2
                    ◇ Q 8 6
                    ♣ A J 7 3
♠ 2                                    ♠ 10 8 6 3
♡ 7 6 4                                ♡ J 10 9
◇ J 10 7 5                             ◇ K 9
♣ 10 9 8 6 2                           ♣ K Q 5 4
                    ♠ A Q J 9 7 5
                    ♡ A K Q
                    ◇ A 4 3 2
                    ♣ —
```

When this deal was played in the 1963 World Championship (Italy-Argentina), a member of the Blue Team won the club lead with the ace (discarding a diamond), drew trumps, and played ace and another diamond putting up dummy's queen. Down one. Of course, declarer cannot afford to duck the second diamond, but the contract should have been brought home anyway.

The correct play is to ruff the first trick in the closed hand, draw trumps, then play hearts. As hearts are 3-3 this establishes two entryless winners in dummy. When the queen of diamonds loses to a *doubleton* king in the East hand, East will be end-played. (This line creates the risk of a second undertrick, but the probability of that is relatively low and the investment for the extra chance at making the contract is worthwhile.)

PROBLEM 83

IMP scoring
East-West vulnerable

NORTH
♠ A 9 6 3
♡ 10 6 3
♢ K 7 4
♣ A Q 9

SOUTH
♠ Q
♡ A K Q J 4
♢ A 3 2
♣ K 6 5 2

SOUTH	WEST	NORTH	EAST
1 ♡	Pass	2 NT	Pass
3 ♣	Pass	3 ♡	Pass
4 ♢	Pass	4 ♠	Pass
6 ♡	Pass	Pass	Pass

West leads the heart nine.

Plan the play.

SOLUTION 83

```
            ♠ A 9 6 3
            ♡ 10 6 3
            ◇ K 7 4
            ♣ A Q 9

♠ K J 5 4 2              ♠ 10 8 7
♡ 9 8                    ♡ 7 5 2
◇ Q 8                    ◇ J 10 9 6 5
♣ J 8 7 3               ♣ 10 4

            ♠ Q
            ♡ A K Q J 4
            ◇ A 3 2
            ♣ K 6 5 2
```

This deal is presented in a popular collection of bridge deals. The recommended line of play is to win two top trumps in the closed hand, then play ace, queen and a third club towards South's king. Once trumps are known to be 3-2, a dummy reversal is clearly a superior chance: heart ace-king, spade ace, spade ruff, club ace, spade ruff, club queen, spade ruff, diamond king, heart ten, etc. Note that declarer should use his club entries to dummy as soon as possible to minimize the chance of a club ruff. If the dimond king is used early, a defender with three trumps, three spades, and two clubs can discard a club on the fourth round of spades and prevent declarer from getting to dummy to draw the last trump. (The East-West cards have been rearranged to emphasize this point.)

PROBLEM 84

Rubber bridge
Neither side vulnerable

NORTH
♠ A 7 5 4 3
♡ 6
◇ 5 4
♣ A 8 6 4 2

SOUTH
♠ K Q J 10 2
♡ A Q 10
◇ A 8 6 2
♣ 3

SOUTH	WEST	NORTH	EAST
1 ♠	Pass	2 ♣	Pass
2 ◇	Pass	4 ♠	Pass
5 ♡	Pass	6 ♠	Pass
Pass	Pass		

West leads the spade nine. East discards the heart four.

Plan the play.

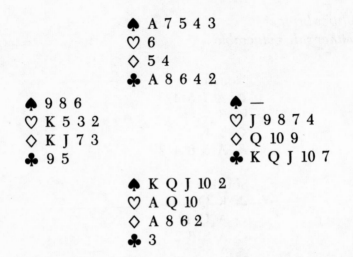

♠ A 7 5 4 3
♡ 6
◇ 5 4
♣ A 8 6 4 2

♠ 9 8 6
♡ K 5 3 2
◇ K J 7 3
♣ 9 5

♠ —
♡ J 9 8 7 4
◇ Q 10 9
♣ K Q J 10 7

♠ K Q J 10 2
♡ A Q 10
◇ A 8 6 2
♣ 3

South should win the opening lead in his hand, lead a club to the ace, and ruff a club with the spade deuce. If this gets through he should try for a complete cross-ruff (hoping to make nine spade tricks and three aces). West must be kept off lead, to avoid the killing lead of another trump, so South should play the ace of diamonds and ace and queen of hearts. If West does not cover, declarer throws dummy's diamond and takes the rest on a cross-ruff. If West covers the heart queen, declarer ruffs, returns to his hand with a high club ruff, and leads the ten of hearts, throwing dummy's diamond.

This plan fails if West has a singleton or void in clubs, or a diamond void, or both heart honors (thus, it has about a 70% chance). This is superior to taking the heart finesse, even though the latter is a bit better than 50% (because of the known spade split). If the heart finesse loses and West returns a trump, declarer lacks the entries to establish and cash a club trick even if the suit breaks 4-3.

PROBLEM 85

Rubber bridge
East-West vulnerable

> **NORTH**
> ♠ 3 2
> ♡ Q J 10 9 6
> ◇ J 10 8 6
> ♣ 6 3
>
> **SOUTH**
> ♠ A K 8 7 5 4
> ♡ A K
> ◇ A K Q 7 2
> ♣ —

SOUTH	WEST	NORTH	EAST
2 ♠	Pass	2 NT	Pass
3 ◇	Pass	4 ◇	Pass
7 ◇	(All pass)		

Wet leads the club queen.

Plan the play.

SOLUTION 85

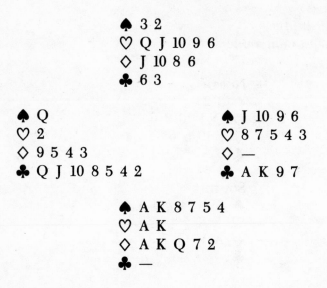

♠ 3 2
♡ Q J 10 9 6
◇ J 10 8 6
♣ 6 3

♠ Q
♡ 2
◇ 9 5 4 3
♣ Q J 10 8 5 4 2

♠ J 10 9 6
♡ 8 7 5 4 3
◇ —
♣ A K 9 7

♠ A K 8 7 5 4
♡ A K
◇ A K Q 7 2
♣ —

There is no problem unless diamonds are 4-0. What can declarer do against such distribution?

South should ruff the first trick with a *high* trump and cash a high trump from the dummy. If East shows out, declarer can ruff a club high, cash the heart ace, lead a high trump and his remaining low diamond to dummy, and draw trumps, unblocking the heart king on the last trump. This guards against a 5-1 heart split.

If East holds all four trumps, declarer must attack spades.

PROBLEM 86

Rubber bridge
Neither side vulnerable

NORTH
♠ 7 6
♡ 8 6 2
◇ 4 2
♣ K J 6 4 3 2

SOUTH
♠ A K Q
♡ A K
◇ Q J 10 9 8
♣ Q 7 5

SOUTH	WEST	NORTH	EAST
2 NT	Pass	3 NT	Pass
Pass	Pass		

West leads the spade four. East plays the jack. *Plan the play (a) at rubber bridge, (b) at matchpoints.*

SOLUTION 86

```
                ♠ 7 6
                ♡ 8 6 2
                ◇ 4 2
                ♣ K J 6 4 3 2
♠ 10 8 5 4 3                    ♠ J 9 2
♡ Q 10 4 3                      ♡ J 9 7 5
◇ A 7 5 3                       ◇ K 6
♣ —                             ♣ A 10 9 8
                ♠ A K Q
                ♡ A K
                ◇ Q J 10 9 8
                ♣ Q 7 5
```

South should win the opening lead, and lead the club *queen*. The club play is unlikely to be relevant unless the suit breaks 4-0. (If clubs are 3-1 or 2-2 and the defense cannot or does not hold up, South has an easy 10 tricks. If there is a successful hold-up, South takes two clubs tricks and switches to diamonds, again scoring 10 tricks.) If this is in fact the club division, by leading the queen of clubs at trick two declarer forces the defense to withhold the club ace—if they take it, South next ducks a club and takes nine tricks. With one club trick in the bag, South switches to diamonds in time to score three spades, two hearts, three diamonds and one club.

Note that if declarer begins clubs by leading to an honor in dummy, the contract can be defeated if East holds all four clubs. He need not duck the first club—declarer cannot possibly bring in the suit—and therefore wins and returns a spade (or heart). The defense still has two diamond entries and can establish and run a major suit.

There is no reason to alter this sure-trick line of play at matchpoints.

PROBLEM 87

Rubber bridge
North-South vulnerable

NORTH
♠ 5 2
♡ K 6 4 3 2
◇ J 8 7 5 4
♣ 9

SOUTH
♠ A K Q 7 6 3
♡ A Q 5
◇ A K 10
♣ A

SOUTH	WEST	NORTH	EAST
2 ♣	4 ♣	Pass	Pass
4 ♠	Pass	5 ♠	Pass
6 ♠	Pass	Pass	Pass

West leads the club king and East plays the deuce. South plays two top spades and West discards a club.

How should South play?

SOLUTION 87

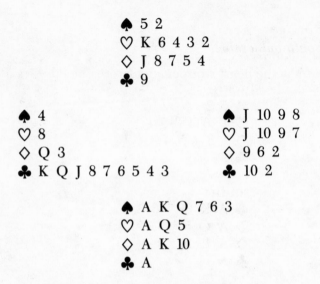

♠ 5 2
♡ K 6 4 3 2
◇ J 8 7 5 4
♣ 9

♠ 4　　　　　　　　　♠ J 10 9 8
♡ 8　　　　　　　　　♡ J 10 9 7
◇ Q 3　　　　　　　　◇ 9 6 2
♣ K Q J 8 7 6 5 4 3　♣ 10 2

♠ A K Q 7 6 3
♡ A Q 5
◇ A K 10
♣ A

The diamond return by East will be harmless, so South should play two more rounds of trumps, discarding diamonds from dummy. He then wins East's return in the closed hand, and tests hearts. If hearts are 3-2 there is no problem. If hearts are adversely stopped, declarer unblocks dummy's diamond jack on the last trump and reaches this position:

NORTH
♡ K 6
◇ 8

SOUTH
♡ 5
◇ K 10

If East has the heart stopper, as in the diagram, South plays to the heart king. At this point East must have a heart left to guard dummy's six, so he cannot have queen and another diamond. Accordingly, declarer should lead a diamond to his king. If West started with only two diamonds, or if East has the queen of diamonds, the diamond ten will be good.

If *West* has the heart stopper, declarer is faced with a guess in diamonds. The best chance seems to be the diamond finesse. If West has one spade, four hearts, and as many as two diamonds, he would have only six clubs— unlikely on the auction. Had there been no bidding, the situation would be even more complex.

PROBLEM 88

Rubber bridge
Neither side vulnerable

NORTH
♠ K 7
♡ 8 6 2
♢ 4 2
♣ K J 8 4 3 2

SOUTH
♠ A Q 6
♡ A K
♢ Q J 10 9 8
♣ Q 6 5

SOUTH	WEST	NORTH	EAST
1 ♢	Pass	2 ♣	Pass
3 NT	(All pass)		

West leads the spade four. East plays the jack. *Plan the play (a) at rubber bridge, (b) at matchpoints.*

SOLUTION 88

♠ K 7
♡ 8 6 2
♢ 4 2
♣ K J 8 4 3 2

♠ 10 8 5 4 3	♠ J 9 2
♡ Q 10 4 3	♡ J 9 7 5
♢ A 7 5 3	♢ K 6
♣ —	♣ A 10 9 7

♠ A Q 6
♡ A K
♢ Q J 10 9 8
♣ Q 6 5

One line of play is to win the spade queen in the closed hand and lead the club queen. If clubs break 2-2 or 3-1, declarer takes 10 tricks easily. If West has four clubs, South still makes five club tricks, and a total of 10 tricks, by finessing dummy's club eight. If East has four clubs and wins the first club, declarer ducks the second round (after unblocking in spades if necessary) and makes nine tricks. If East has four clubs and ducks the first club, South switches to diamonds. If the defense wins this, they cannot prevent South from unblocking in spades and scoring nine tricks. If the defense ducks one diamond (to cut declarer's transportation), South returns to clubs. If East ducks the second club, South goes back to diamonds for at least nine tricks. If East wins the second club, he must return a spade (to prevent the establishment of clubs) and South now reverts to diamonds.

Another line is slightly superior in that it gives better chances for an overtrick while still assuring the contract, and is thus the best play at either form of bridge. Declarer should win the spade king in dummy and lead a club to the queen. If clubs are not 4-0, the position is equivalent to the previous problem.

If West has four clubs, he must duck two clubs (because of dummy's eight), and declarer can now switch to diamonds and make ten tricks. If East has four clubs he is *forced* to duck the first club (where he had an option on the other line). South now switches to diamonds. A heart shift will probably hold declarer to his contract, but East is likely to continue spades. Now declarer can play for an overtrick by establishing diamonds and then going after a second club trick. This loses only if East has five spades—wildly unlikely when he holds four clubs and West led spades.

PROBLEM 89

Rubber bridge
Neither side vulnerable

> NORTH
> ♠ 8 6 4 3
> ♡ 8 7 6
> ◊ 7 5 3 2
> ♣ A 7
>
> SOUTH
> ♠ A K Q J 10
> ♡ A K Q
> ◊ K J 4
> ♣ K 5

SOUTH	WEST	NORTH	EAST
2 ♣	Pass	2 ◊	Pass
2 ♠	Pass	4 ♠	Pass
4 NT	Pass	5 ◊	Pass
6 ♠	(All pass)		

West leads the spade deuce. East plays the five.

Plan the play.

SOLUTION 89

♠ 8 6 4 3
♡ 8 7 6
♢ 7 5 3 2
♣ A 7

♠ 9 2
♡ J 9 5 4 3
♢ Q 8
♣ Q 10 8 2

♠ 7 5
♡ 10 2
♢ A 10 9 6
♣ J 9 6 4 3

♠ A K Q J 10
♡ A K Q
♢ K J 4
♣ K 5

This is not a good contract, but the fault does not lie in South's aggressive bidding. Partner, as usual, holds the wrong side-suit distribution. Still, South must take his best chance.

The basic line is to draw trumps, cash the hearts and clubs ending in dummy, and lead a diamond. If East holds (a), the doubleton ace-queen of diamonds, or (b), the singleton ace of diamonds, the hand plays itself.

If East plays a low diamond, South can play the jack (hoping that West holds (c), the singleton ace), or the king (hoping that West holds (d), the doubleton queen-ten). The latter play is superior not only in that holding (d) is slightly more likely than holding (c), but because West may fail to unblock with (e), some other doubleton-queen holding, or East may duck with ace doubleton.

These chances are all slight. Declarer can almost certainly improve his chances by drawing trumps, leading a club to the ace, and leading a diamond to the king. This still makes the contract against (a) and (d), unless in the latter case West can unblock on the hearts. And although it gives up (b) and (c), it increases the chance that West will fail to unblock from (e). Drawing trumps (which would be the natural play) but not eliminating the other suits seems to give West the maximum chance to make this error.